# TRIUMPH
# OVER
# TRAUMA
## WORKBOOK

Gregory L. Jantz, PhD

with Keith Wall

# TRIUMPH OVER TRAUMA WORKBOOK

The 12-Week Journey to Lasting
Wholeness and Healing

ILLUMIFY
MEDIA.COM

# TRIUMPH
# OVER
# TRAUMA
## WORKBOOK

The views and opinions expressed in this book are those of the author and do not
necessarily reflect the official policy or position of Illumify Media Global.

Published by
Illumify Media Global
www.IllumifyMedia.com
*"Let's bring your book to life!"*

Paperback ISBN: 978-1-959099-19-2

Typeset by Art Innovations (http://www.artinnovations.in/)
Cover design by Debbie Lewis

*Printed in the United States of America*

# Contents

# You Shall Overcome

"I don't think I can ever get over this."

"I'm in so much pain that I can't go on."

"I trudge through each day, weighed down by what happened to me."

In my thirty-five years as a mental health professional, I have heard statements like these countless times. They're uttered by hurting people who have experienced a painful past—caused by others, their own choices, or unfortunate circumstances. These men and women feel mired in their pain with little hope for brighter days ahead.

But there is hope—hope in your inner strength, abundant resilience, and an all-powerful God.

So my responses to people's pleas of desperation and pain usually go like this:

"You *can* get over this time of hurt and heartache. I believe you can and you will."

"Your pain is real and deep, but it doesn't have to hold you captive. It doesn't have to determine who you are."

"Life brings us plenty of challenges, but you can persevere and overcome. Each day can be a joyful adventure for you."

These are the messages I want to convey to you too!

We know that traumatic experiences happen to nearly everyone, at some time, in some form. Many people suffer from the aftereffects of trauma—including depression, anxiety, addiction, panic attacks, and insomnia—for years or even a lifetime. Robbed of joy and hope, these people struggle tremendously, often finding their relationships, work productivity, and life satisfaction compromised.

It doesn't need to be this way! With expert guidance, intentional effort, and a strong support system, anyone suffering from the effects of recent or long-ago trauma can experience lasting wellness, wholeness, and joyfulness. Hope, help, and healing are available to anyone, no matter how painful their circumstances and how desperate they feel to break free.

The message woven throughout the *Triumph over Trauma* book and reaffirmed in the pages of this workbook is this:

> **Brokenness following a traumatic event is never a one-way ticket or a life sentence. You are certainly *changed* by trauma and can never undo what happened to you. It becomes a part of who you are, like everything else you've ever experienced.**
>
> **But it is a blatant lie to envision yourself like Humpty Dumpty lying in pieces on the ground, without hope of ever being whole again. You can live the life you've longed for, with close relationships, inner peace, and energy to pursue your dreams.**

You can be free from thoughts, feelings, and habits that drag you down rather than lift you up. You can learn to draw the life-numbing poison out of your past pain, present problems, and future fear.

I am not giving you a pep talk or offering snappy slogans to help you feel better momentarily. The last thing you need is advice that rings hallow, or bromides that promise much and deliver little. If you've been struggling with painful memories and past hurts for any length of time, you have likely heard all kinds of recommendations that didn't bring you much improvement. Worse, you've probably heard plenty of clichés from well-meaning (but unhelpful) people: "Just let it go . . . . This too shall pass. . . . Hold on to your faith."

I know that working through traumatic experiences takes patience, fierce determination, courage to confront painful issues, openness to new ideas, and a commitment to change long-standing patterns of behavior.

Another essential element is needed to overcome the aftereffects of past pain: Hope.

I have counseled thousands of people who needed help coping with pain and fear of every kind: anxiety, depression, guilt, anger, addiction, and the emotional scars of physical and psychological abuse. Early in my career, I often felt dismayed by the epic scope of battles people waged within themselves and the elusive struggle to achieve true healing. It seemed to me that lasting wellness was a treasure many seek but few ever find.

Then I realized something vitally important. Many of the hurting people I counseled were eager—or desperate—to overcome their troubles but lacked the key ingredient of hope. By the time these people began therapy with me or sought treatment at the clinic I direct, they had lived with their condition for so long and tried so many unfruitful treatment options that optimism had all but vanished. Distress and despair, usually caused by a variety of factors, were compounded by a fundamental lack of hopefulness and confidence that anything would ever change.

This led me to make *hope* a cornerstone of all the therapy, speaking, writing, research, and treatment planning I do. In 2014, we changed the named of our Seattle-area treatment facility after clients said, "This is a place of hope." That's exactly what we wanted and thus the name stuck, now called The Center: A Place of Hope. My team and I also adopted Jeremiah 29:11-14 as our clinic's guiding Scripture passage:

> "For I know the plans I have for you," declares the Lord, "plans to prosper you and not to harm you, plans to give you hope and a future. Then you will call upon me and come and pray to me, and I will listen to you. You will seek me and find me when you seek me with all your heart. I will be found by you," declares the Lord, "and will bring you back from captivity."

I encourage you to reflect on these life-changing words and embrace them as your touchstone as your pursue your own emotional, spiritual, and physical wellness. After all, people consistently dealing with hurts and wounds often feel that they are in "captivity" of sorts—trapped and immobilized by a force bigger than themselves. That's where trauma often leaves people.

But God will indeed bring you back. Hurting people often do not feel enthused about the future, if they can envision one at all. But God will help you renew your dreams and refresh your energy to achieve them.

As foundational as hope is to true healing, there are many other indispensible steps to take on the journey. And these steps form the twelve weeks' of exercises, assessments, and reflections in the pages ahead. In addition to the need for hope, I realized something else many years ago: Most approaches to trauma recovery focus on a particular approach, using *one* technique to address a complex mental-health conundrum. Care providers tend to use their favorites as "singular" fixes to complex struggles that are never caused by one thing alone. Most frequently, this means taking medication, seeing a counselor for talk therapy, starting a specialized diet regimen, or participating in cognitive behavioral therapy.

While each of these individual approaches can be helpful and sometimes needed, I believe that lasting healing occurs through a whole-person, multi-faceted approach. The whole-person treatment approach I have employed for decades recognizes that every human being is a unique constellation of emotional, physical, intellectual, relational, and spiritual dimensions.

By addressing and engaging each element using evidence-based techniques, we promote the healing of the entire person. This is why my whole-person approach includes:

☐ Working through the process of forgiveness for hurts and heartaches

☐ Harnessing your thoughts to provide a positive, empowering outlook

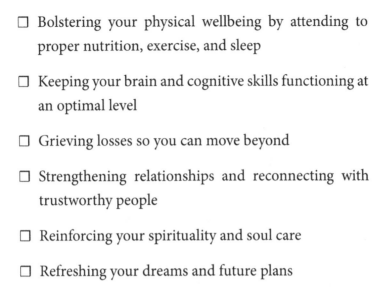

☐ Bolstering your physical wellbeing by attending to proper nutrition, exercise, and sleep

☐ Keeping your brain and cognitive skills functioning at an optimal level

☐ Grieving losses so you can move beyond

☐ Strengthening relationships and reconnecting with trustworthy people

☐ Reinforcing your spirituality and soul care

☐ Refreshing your dreams and future plans

These topics were discussed in detail in the *Triumph over Trauma* book, where I present an array of scientific research studies, psychological principles, spiritual insights, real-life stories, and practical applications. With this companion workbook, I am inviting you to dive in and dig deep into the *reasons* for your current distress and, more important, the *remedies* that will empower you to move forward toward freedom and joy. Think of me as your guide and coach through the journey. I will point you in the right direction and offer plenty of suggestions . . . but the challenge is for you to take one step after another through the exercises ahead.

You might choose to use this workbook by yourself, with a friend, or in a small-group setting (I provide suggestions for group use in the pages ahead). You also might be someone who prefers to work through the exercises in one sitting, or you might choose to spread out the activities throughout the week. You might go back and forth between the book and workbook, or you might complete them at separate times.

My encouragement: Whatever works best for you, do it! I have created this workbook to be flexible and adaptable for your ideal use and maximize benefit. If you invest yourself in these pages, you will find yourself a giant step toward wholeness and healing after twelve weeks.

* * *

I know that addressing painful past events can stir up strong emotions. Feelings long buried might come to the surface. That is a natural part of the healing experience. Take your time. Be kind to yourself along the way. Lean on trustworthy people. Seek God's comfort throughout each day.

Hundreds of my clients, who have put the ideas in this workbook into practice, are living proof that a whole new way of being is as near to your ability to hope. They have learned, as you can, that life need not be filled with distress, shame, anxiety, depression, regret, and fear. Every moment can be filled with wonder, exhilaration, optimism, and gratitude.

I leave you with these words from the Old Testament, fully confident that you will someday soon proclaim them in your own life: "Those who hope in the Lord will renew their strength. They will soar on wings like eagles; they will run and not grow weary, they will walk and not be faint" (Isaiah 40:31).

Your pain will not prevail.

Your fortitude and your faith will empower to overcome.

# Guidance for Groups

Healing can and does happen individually . . . but *most* healing happens within community. People struggling with the painful aftermath of traumatic events often feel isolated, alone, and misunderstood. That's why groups centered on sharing personal experiences and discussing steps toward healing can be so powerful.

Such groups are greatly needed because so many people endure some form of trauma, causing an array of mental health issues. Research from the Centers for Disease Control reveals that:

- ☐ 75 percent of Americans have experienced a traumatic event and 6.7 percent of those individuals have had post-traumatic stress disorder (PTSD) in their lifetime.

- ☐ Two-thirds of children in this country experience at least one traumatic event by age 16.

- ☐ In the United States, approximately five million children experience some form of traumatic event each year.[1]

Despite the prevalence of trauma-related difficulties, some people never address their struggles because doing so feels too painful and overwhelming. Others dismiss their hardships, as if they should "just get over it," have more faith, or act happy so they don't bring everyone else down with them. Worse, many trauma survivors feel deeply flawed at their core, falsely believing that their struggles make them different from others or even inferior.

A group centered on the topic of trauma recovery should, above all, seek to be loving, gracious, and accepting. Everyone on earth struggles with something, whether depression, anxiety, physical ailments, relationship disappointments, spiritual disillusionment, addictive behaviors, and on and on. We are truly fellow travelers on the journey toward wholeness.

With this in mind, here are several suggestions for using this workbook effectively in a group setting:

☐ It's best for one person to serve as facilitator, setting the tone for the gathering, guiding the discussion, and keeping the meeting focused.

☐ The facilitator should prepare ahead of time by reviewing the week's exercises and deciding which topics and questions would be appropriate and helpful within a group setting.

☐ Be sensitive to the discussion process. Try to give everyone an opportunity to speak, and when necessary, gently redirect the focus of those who tend to dominate a discussion.

☐ Be careful not to put anyone on the spot or make anyone feel pressured to share. The questions and assessments in this workbook cover some very personal and sensitive topics. Encourage group members to share their answers and thoughts if they feel comfortable doing so—and give the freedom to stay quiet if they wish to.

☐ Use this workbook in conjunction with the *Triumph over Trauma* book if possible. Ideally, the two go hand-in-hand, with the book providing thorough explanations of the whole-person approach and the workbook following up practical exercises. However, each section of the workbook begins with an "At a Glance" summary of the corresponding book chapter(s), followed by an "Essential Ideas" portion. So even those who have not read the book, or missed particular chapters, can get up to speed quickly and find the discussion helpful.

☐ The sections of the workbook that best lend themselves to group discussion are: "Essential Ideas . . . and Your Insights" and "Dig Deeper." Both of these include several questions and space for group members' responses. Some participants might like to share their journaling response from the "Change Your Story, Change Your Life" section. The bottom line is to use *any* of this material that will be most helpful in engaging your group members in the discussion process.

# The Truth Will Set You Free

*Overcoming Trauma Requires Honesty and Courage*

**Review chapter 1 in the *Triumph over Trauma* book**

## Week 1 at a Glance

Trauma comes in many shapes and sizes. You don't have to have lived in a warzone to be impacted by trauma. I have met many people in the grip of debilitating symptoms of trauma who say things like, "But I'm not a soldier or anything like that. Yes, I had a difficult childhood, but other people go through things much worse. So I can't figure out why I feel so broken."

Yet the kinds of painful experiences that can leave us feeling stuck and broken are many. Combat, sexual assault, childhood abuse, domestic violence, and public shootings are obvious traumatic events, but divorce, illness, or losing someone we love can leave us traumatized as well.

The truth is, many kinds of painful circumstances or events can leave us feeling wounded and unsafe long after the event has passed. When this happens, we can fall into despair, believing that we are broken beyond repair and that nothing can help us regain what we've lost, such as our sense of safety, trust, peace, and vitality.

The good news is that nothing could be further from the truth. You are not too broken to experience hope and healing from the events that have left you reeling. Your past does not need to continue defining and limiting your future. You do not need to resign yourself to the trauma-driven pain with which you now live.

## Essential Ideas . . . and Your insights

1. **Trauma leaves scars that will never completely go away, but you can have a fuller, richer life because of your experiences.** If the first part of that sentence is easier to believe than the second part, I get it. Trauma leaves scars. You know this is true because you are living with them. But the second part of the sentence is just as true. I know this because I have seen countless people embrace the kind of fuller, richer life that can be yours as well (and the fact that you are reading this workbook tells me that you believe it's possible too).

   **Your response:** How is your life today impacted by traumatic events or circumstances in your past? How ready are you to begin to experience new hope and healing? To what extent are you willing to go to experience a brighter future? Are you willing to invest the time and energy to complete the weeks in this workbook?

   _____

   _____

   _____

   _____

2. **Trauma survivors often feel unjustified shame, guilt, and remorse.** An essential component for healing is to recognize unhealthy emotions that don't belong to you and replace them with healthy

ones that do belong to you. I know this is easier said than done—especially because over time unhealthy emotions can feel familiar and even comfortable (despite the pain that they bring us). But releasing them is not only possible, it is a foundational step to experiencing the peace and freedom you deserve.

**Your response:** Have you experienced shame, guilt, or remorse as a result of events in your past? When you think about replacing these with healthier emotions, what is your gut response? Fear? Dread? Relief? Hope? Joy?

---

---

---

---

3.  **Hope is a powerful ally in the quest to work through heartache and restore damaged emotions.** While it's true that wise counsel, courage, support from friends, and healthier habits are part of the healing equation, hope is absolutely indispensable. If you never allow yourself to experience hope (and even anticipation), then counseling, friends, and improved habits are limited in how much they can help.

    What's more, I believe God is the ultimate restorer and healer of broken people. As a person of faith, I am convinced that God wants each of us to be fulfilled, enjoy rewarding relationships, and grow into our full potential. As Scripture assures us, "And the God of all grace, who called you to his eternal glory in Christ, after you have suffered a little while, will himself restore you and make you strong, firm and steadfast" (1 Peter 5:10).

    **Your response:** It's possible that you are already aware of things that make you feel more hopeful. This might include reading stories of other overcomers, talking a walk in nature, reading scripture or praying. Is there a "hope-seeding" action you can take today? How willing are you to invite God into your healing journey?

_____

_____

_____

_____

## Taking Stock

How is trauma impacting your life? Let's take stock. How often do you experience the following:

1 = very little
2 = often but not regularly
3 = on a daily basis

1.  Depression and/or sadness

    1        2        3

2.  Emotional numbness

    1        2        3

3.  Anxiety

    1        2        3

4.  Low self-esteem

    1        2        3

5.  Irritability or anger

    1        2        3

6. Mood swings

           1      2      3

7. Lack of focus

           1      2      3

8. Unhealthy habits or coping choices

           1      2      3

9. Substance abuse (food, alcohol, or drugs)

           1      2      3

10. Self-harm, including cutting, burning, unsafe sexual practices

           1      2      3

11. Fatigue

           1      2      3

12. Inability to trust others

           1      2      3

13. Nagging sense of impending doom

           1      2      3

14. Nightmares or recurring dreams

           1      2      3

15. Unexplained physical pain

           1      2      3

16. Suicidal thoughts

           1      2      3

17. Denial

          1       2       3

18. Shame

          1       2       3

19. Flashbacks

          1       2       3

20. Dissociation

          1       2       3

21. Memory problems

          1       2       3

Trauma can impact your physical and emotional health in many ways, which is why the steps you have taken to read the book *Triumph over Trauma* and complete this workbook are important. As you embrace the opportunities for reflection and action in this book and workbook, you truly can experience triumph over trauma.

## Change Your Story, Change Your Life

1. What is the story you tell yourself about the traumatic experiences in your life? Do you blame yourself? Blame others? Believe you were/ are a victim? Believe you are too broken to experience a healthy life? Have hope for the future? Write about what you believe:

_____

_____

_____

_____

_____

_____

_____

_____

_____

_____

## Dig Deeper

1. Describe one or more of the painful experiences in your past that may be impacting your life today.

_____

_____

_____

_____

_____

2. In what ways do you feel your daily life is impacted by painful events in your life?

_____

_____

_____

_____

_____

3. If you had not experienced these traumatic events or circumstances, how do you think your life would be or feel different?

_____

_____

_____

_____

_____

4. What interventions have you tried in the past, and how helpful were they?

_____

_____

_____

_____

_____

5. What role does faith play in your life? What do you believe about God's role in your life before, during, or after painful events or circumstances in your life?

_____

_____

---

---

---

## First Steps, Next Steps

Now it's time to get practical. We've explored many issues that prompted you to ponder and process. Let's put those thoughts into action. We'll provide several steps forward, and then it's your turn to determine three additional actions you will take this week.

1.  Chapter 1 of the book *Triumph over Trauma* identifies four actions you can take to begin your journey toward healing. If you haven't read the book, I encourage you do to so—and to take the actions in these chapters. Like this one:

    *Share your story. People who have experienced a traumatic event tend to feel isolated and alone in their pain. Fearing that no one else can relate, trauma survivors often keep their stories tucked away inside. The effects of trauma are magnified in isolation. Research shows that the symptoms of trauma are reduced when survivors connect with other people but taking that first step and reaching out to someone can be difficult. Consider starting small by writing out your story. When you're ready, share it with a trusted friend, church leader, or counselor.*

---

---

---

_____

_____

If you haven't taken one of the actions described in chapter 1, do it now.

Describe the chapter 1 action you have completed. What impact did it have on you? What would you tell a close friend about the experience? Would you recommend it to someone you love struggling with trauma? Why or why not?

_____

_____

_____

_____

_____

2. Can you think of someone (a personal friend, family member, or public figure) who has experienced trauma in their past and gone on to heal and thrive--and perhaps even inspire others? Describe what impacts you the most about their story.

_____

_____

_____

_____

_____

3.  Because hope is such an important dynamic in your journey toward healing, identify a symbol or tangible object that represents "hope" to you. What is that item or symbol? Describe it below, then find a way to showcase that symbol or item in a place where you can see it every day.

    _____

    _____

    _____

    _____

    _____

4.  Your turn. What additional steps do you intend to take this week to move toward wellness?

    a.  _____

        _____

        _____

    b.  _____

        _____

        _____

    c.  _____

        _____

        _____

## Closing Reflections

If painful events in your life have left you reeling, you can find solid ground again. You don't have to justify the impact of trauma on your life to anyone. Even if there is someone in your life telling you that what you experienced "wasn't that bad" and that you should "just get over it," listen to your heart. Acknowledge the impact of the past and know that you deserve to do whatever it takes for you to find hope and healing.

Most of all, cling to hope. You have already taken some important steps on your healing journey. You can do this. I believe in you.

## Scripture for Meditation

"The Lord is near to the brokenhearted and saves the crushed in spirit."

PSALM 34:18

## Wise Words to Awaken Your Spirit

"You deserve freedom. You owe it to yourself. You are anything but selfish whenever you decide to stand up for yourself!"

MYRIAM BEN SALEM

## Journal Your Journey

This week you are going to be taking steps forward, forging new habits, and letting go of old ones. Will these things make a difference? Will you be able to discern any changes in how you feel and what you think?

This page is here for you to journal about the journey. What works? What doesn't? You'll know what to keep doing because you'll have your adventure documented in the pages of this workbook. Use this space to ask questions, make lists, doodle, write about your progress, record milestones, and write your forgiveness statement(s).

Let the adventure begin!

_____

_____

_____

_____

_____

_____

_____

_____

_____

_____

_____

_____

_____

_____

_____

_____

_____

_____

_____

_____

_____

_____

_____

_____

_____

_____

_____

_____

_____

_____

_____

# Hope Amid Heartache

*Trauma Happens to Nearly Everyone—and Healing Can Too*

**Review chapter 2 in the *Triumph over Trauma* book**

## Week 2 at a Glance

Traumatic events can happen to anyone. No matter who you are—or how intentional you are about keeping yourself and your loved ones safe—you can experience the devastating, life-altering effects of trauma. In fact, studies show that seven out of ten adults in America have experienced trauma at least once in their lifetimes; that more than 13 million Americans suffer from PTSD; and that women are twice as likely as men to develop PTSD.

If you still aren't convinced that past trauma may be at the root of the pain keeping you from living your best life, consider this: we can be traumatized by things that didn't even happen to us. When we witness extreme suffering in the lives of others, we rarely walk away unscathed. Our souls are wounded. Survivor's guilt is one of the ways "secondhand trauma" affects many people. Those who have survived horrendous events that took a toll on others can find themselves plagued by guilt, shame, self-blame, self-destructive behaviors, and even thoughts of suicide.

What's more, traumatic events can wreak havoc in entire communities. Natural disasters, economic devastation, and global events such as pandemics are a few examples of painful events that can send entire communities—even nations—reeling.

The realization that trauma is a universal experience can be helpful in two ways: First, we may find comfort in knowing that we are not alone in our suffering. Second, the universal nature of trauma can remind us that, as an inescapable part of life, pain doesn't necessarily mean we did anything "wrong," or that we are in some way deserving of the wounds we carry.

## Essential Ideas . . . and Your Insights

Just as trauma happens more than we think, healing happens more often than we realize as well. Here are three essential ideas in this chapter:

1.  **Healing happens—for anyone willing to choose it and work for it.**
    We can hang on to the brokenness, believing healing is beyond our reach, but the truth is that hope and healing really are possible. To take matters further, hope and healing aren't just possible, they are well within our grasp.

    Unlike trauma, however, healing typically doesn't happen "to us"—we must take an active role in pursuing the vibrant life we long for. And when we do, we will discover that it's well worth the effort.

    **Your response:** Are you willing to be intentional about pursuing a life of wholeness, or do you believe "time heals all wounds" and that your best bet is to wait for healing to happen? Have you met people who—after decades of pain—are still waiting passively for time to finally "kick in" and do its magic? What might someone who has felt broken for years, even decades, say about the idea that given enough time, healing occurs on its own?

    _____

    _____

_____

_____

_____

2.  **Healing happens—when we treat the whole person, not just a set of symptoms.** Trauma doesn't "color in the lines." For example, physical trauma impacts more than just our bodies, psychological trauma impacts more than our mental health, and so on. All trauma—regardless of where and how it was originally experienced—can and does create dysfunction in every area of our lives, including our bodies, mental health, relationships, finances, spirituality, and more. And if we try to cope with all that pain via unhealthy behaviors and even addictions, we create even more trauma for ourselves, creating a never-ending circle of trauma and pain.

    This is why treating trauma must include a whole-person approach to every aspect of life, including brain chemistry, relationships, self-talk, physical ailments, destructive patterns, and more. When we are reeling from painful experiences, we must identify and treat the far-reaching tentacles of that trauma.

    **Your response:** What do you think about the idea that many of your struggles—even if they are in areas on the surface that don't seem related to past trauma—can be rooted in the trauma you have experienced? Can you identify possible links between your past trauma and current struggles? Describe how they may be related.

_____

_____

_____

_____

3. **Healing happens—when we take God at his word.** In the Old Testament, the psalmist writes, "How good it is to sing praises to our God, how pleasant and fitting to praise Him!" Why? Because "he heals the brokenhearted and binds up their wounds" (147:1, 3).

   Wherever you are in your faith journey, you don't have to go it alone. Your trauma may have left you with questions for God—or even anger toward him—and that's okay. You don't have to have all the answers or be fully at peace with God to look at his promises in Scripture and make a bold choice in faith to believe what they say. Give God a chance to prove his promises to you.

   **Your response:** Faith doesn't always make "sense"—at least not to the mind. But even as our minds wrestle with doubt, our spirits can step up and say, "I'm making a choice—despite the hurt and pain in my life—to believe that God has healing and goodness in store for me." How willing are you to make that choice? If your first thought is *not very*, why not? What downside do you associate with making the choice to believe that God can play a role in the healing of your past trauma?

   _____

   _____

   _____

   _____

   _____

## Taking Stock

Are lies keeping you from accepting the truth that healing happens for many people—and that it can happen for you? Are there things you believe are holding you back from accepting this truth?

Respond to each of the following statements:

1 = No, I don't believe this

2 = My head knows this isn't true, but my heart believes it

3 = Yes, I believe this

1. Deep inside, I believe I deserve the traumatic thing that happened to me

$$1 \qquad 2 \qquad 3$$

2. I'm too broken to experience healing

$$1 \qquad 2 \qquad 3$$

3. I've had hope in the past, but I don't now because I don't want to be disappointed again

$$1 \qquad 2 \qquad 3$$

4. Other people will never let me forget what happened

$$1 \qquad 2 \qquad 3$$

5. I'm stuck in this place forever

$$1 \qquad 2 \qquad 3$$

6. Secretly, I believe it is my fault

$$1 \qquad 2 \qquad 3$$

7. Healing is for other people, but not for me

$$1 \qquad 2 \qquad 3$$

8. I'm beyond help

$$1 \qquad 2 \qquad 3$$

9.  What happened to me wasn't that bad—I have no right to feel
    the pain I feel

    1        2        3

10. God doesn't really care about what happened to me

    1        2        3

## Change Your Story, Change Your Life

1.  What is the story you tell yourself about your chances of living a
    happy, healthy life? Write about what you believe:

    _____

    _____

    _____

    _____

    _____

    _____

    _____

    _____

    _____

    _____

    _____

    _____

2. Now write out a different narrative you want to embrace. Where do you want to end up? Describe your ideal future and destination. Describe actions or milestones in your journey to that destination.

_____

_____

_____

_____

_____

_____

_____

_____

_____

_____

_____

_____

_____

_____

_____

_____

_____

_____

# Dig Deeper

1. Revisit the circled beliefs in the "Taking Stock" section. Can you pinpoint any "benefit" these statements might provide for you? For example, do they feel familiar and comfortable? Might they protect you from getting your hopes too high? Does your brokenness bring you attention that feels good?

   _____

   _____

   _____

   _____

   _____

   _____

2. Consider healthy ways to process your emotions—and act on your intentions. This might mean pursuing therapy with a qualified counselor, meeting regularly with a trusted friend, or joining a support group. Describe your plan:

   _____

   _____

   _____

   _____

   _____

   _____

   _____

3.  Traumatic events cause a "ripple effect" of difficult emotions. Revisit a time when worry, anxiety, or stress created a hardship in your life. Write about the experience, and create a new ending to the story.

_____

_____

_____

_____

_____

_____

## First Steps, Next Steps

Now it's time to get practical. We've explored many issues that prompted you to ponder and process. Let's put those thoughts into action. I'll provide several steps forward, and then it's your turn to determine three additional actions you will take this week.

1.  Chapter 2 of the book *Triumph over Trauma* invites you to make an honest assessment of your whole-person health. If you haven't read the book, I encourage you do to so—and to take the assessment in Chapter 2.

_____

_____

_____

Based on that assessment, identify one thing you can do to pursue better health in each of the following areas of your life:

Physical health: _____

Emotional health: _____

Mental health: _____

Spiritual health: _____

Relational health: _____

2.  Once again, revisit the circled beliefs from the "Taking Stock" section that may be keeping you from accepting the truth that healing happens for many people—and that it can happen for you.

    Is there someone you know and trust who can help you process these beliefs? Write down the names of one or more people whose perspective you value and with whom you might be willing to talk about the things you believe that are robbing you of hope:

    _____

    _____

    _____

    _____

    _____

    _____

    _____

3.  Call, email, or text one of those people right now and set up a time
    when you can talk. Be prepared to share with them some of the
    limiting beliefs that rob you of hope, and to consider their perspective
    and words of encouragement.

    Write the date and time of your conversation below:

    _____

    _____

    _____

    _____

    _____

4.  Your turn. What additional steps do you intend to take this week to
    move toward wellness?

    a.  _____

        _____

        _____

    b.  _____

        _____

        _____

    c.  _____

        _____

        _____

## Closing Reflections

We're all familiar with the idiom, "Which came first, the chicken or the egg?" When it comes to healing from trauma, we don't need to ask which comes first, hope or progress, because they both inspire each other. When we have hope, progress follows. And when we make progress, hope grows.

We can stall the entire healing process, however, when we hang on to ideas that undermine and destroy our hope.

Protect your hope. And one of the ways you can do that is welcoming the influence of people in your life who can help you discard limiting beliefs and embrace a healthier vision of what your life can become.

And if you are still wondering what role faith and God might play in restoring your hope, consider the verse below. It was Paul's prayer for the church in Rome, and it is my prayer for you.

## Scripture for Meditation

"May the God of hope fill you with all joy and peace as you
trust in him, so that you may overflow with hope by the power
of the Holy Spirit."

ROMANS 15:13

## Wise Words to Awaken Your Spirit

"Let your hopes, not your hurts, shape your future."

ROBERT H. SCHULLER

# Journal Your Journey

This week you are going to be taking steps forward, forging new habits, and letting go of old ones. Will these things make a difference? Will you be able to discern any changes in how you feel and what you think?

This page is here for you to journal about the journey. What works? What doesn't? You'll know what to keep doing because you'll have your adventure documented in the pages of this workbook. Use this space to ask questions, make lists, doodle, write about your progress, record milestones, and write your forgiveness statement(s).

Let the adventure begin!

_____

_____

_____

_____

_____

_____

_____

_____

_____

_____

_____

_____

_____

_____

_____

_____

_____

_____

_____

_____

_____

_____

_____

_____

_____

_____

_____

_____

_____

_____

_____

# Ten Truths about Trauma

*A Candid Look at Complex Issues*

**Review chapter 3 in the *Triumph over Trauma* book**

## Week 3 at a Glance

Last week we talked about how your beliefs can either undermine or accelerate your hope, which can make all the difference in the world as you begin to pursue freedom from the pain that has been wreaking havoc in your life.

Understanding the truth about what trauma is—and what it isn't—is another important part of your healing journey.

Trauma is any shocking event that strips a person of his or her fundamental sense of safety—and this isn't limited to physical safety. When we feel threatened or experience loss in any area of our life that defines our sense of self, trauma can be the result.

## Essential Ideas . . . and Your Insight

1. **Traumatic events don't impact everyone the same way.** Remember my definition of trauma from the previous section? *We experience*

*trauma when we feel threatened or experience loss in any area of our life that defines our sense of self.* That's important because not everyone defines their sense of self in the same way. That means that the exact same event experienced by two different people can pose a different threat level, represent a different level of loss, and result in completely different levels of trauma—or no trauma at all.

**Your response:** Are there people in your life who believe you should "be over it" by now? How do their opinions make you feel? Do you believe them?

_____

_____

_____

_____

2. **When it comes to triumphing over trauma, approaches that don't work include waiting passively for time to heal, looking for shortcuts, or trying to muscle your way through via sheer grit and determination.**

   **Your response:** Most people don't delve into the painful aspects of their lives, and that's understandable. Do you think you're more likely to take the passive approach, look for shortcuts, or try to tough things out? How willing are you to look at traumatic experiences, even though painful?

_____

_____

_____

_____

3.  **Trauma isn't a life sentence.** Think back on your life. There's a good chance that at some point in the past you told yourself, "My life is ruined, and I'll never experience joy again," only to go on to heal and thrive again. You might argue, "Yes, but what I experienced then was nothing compared to the pain I have experienced since then." And you might have a good point. Yet resilience is like a muscle, and if you have ever experienced what it's like to thrive again after a great hurt, take heart. You can do it this time too.

    **Your response:** What hurts have you overcome in the past? What specifically provided the strength and courage to address your pain?

    _____

    _____

    _____

    _____

## Taking Stock

Chapter 3 of the *Triumph over Trauma* book includes stories of people who experienced trauma following seven very different kinds of experiences:

- ☐ A woman withdrew from life after being jilted on her wedding day

- ☐ A doctor sank into anxiety and depression during the traumatic experience of his wife's breast cancer diagnosis and treatment

- ☐ Parents fell into despair for not being able to save a daughter who died of a heroin overdose

☐ A former soldier with PTSD experienced flashbacks and panic attacks that landed him in the ER

☐ A pilot experienced insomnia, flashbacks, depression, and addictions after a plane he was flying crashed and took the life of a close friend

☐ After being shot on a call, a paramedic completed rehab and jumped right back into work—only to find that the near-death experience had traumatized her more than she realized

☐ A nursing student who was sexually assaulted believed that any semblance of a normal life following the assault was impossible

These stories illustrated various truths about trauma, but they also reveal how broad the spectrum of traumatizing events can be.

What's more, trauma can be cumulative. For instance, in the story of the woman abandoned on her wedding day, Angie had struggled with social anxiety since childhood. Her painful wedding day experience was the culmination of years of lesser social traumas that added layers of significance to the humiliation and rejection.

Can you identify other traumatic experiences that may have occurred in different stages of your life? Looking back, you might be tempted to think, "That was no big deal," but if it left you feeling unsafe—and navigating the aftermath of those feelings long after the event—write it down.

Childhood Years: _____

_____

Teen Years: _____
_____

Adult Years: _____
_____

# Change Your Story, Change Your Life

1.  What is the story you tell yourself about the painful experiences in
    your past?

_____

_____

_____

_____

_____

_____

_____

_____

_____

_____

_____

_____

_____

2. Now write out a different narrative you want to embrace. If your feelings of trauma are real, if healing takes more than time, and if healing is absolutely possible, what new story might you tell yourself about your healing journey and your future?

_____

_____

_____

_____

_____

_____

_____

_____

_____

## Dig Deeper

1. If time by itself is not a remedy for trauma, what intentional steps, actions, or resources do you believe can contribute to healing? Of those, which are you willing to take?

_____

_____

_____

_____

2. Who do you blame for the trauma in your life? Yourself? Others? God? Blame is in itself a painful situation. If any feelings of blame could be addressed and eliminated, would you feel freer? What impact might that sense of freedom have on your healing journey?

_____

_____

_____

_____

_____

_____

_____

3. Earlier we discussed that there are no shortcuts to trauma recovery. Have you tried to "shortcut" the process? Do you know people who have tried to shortcut the process in their own lives? What are some of the ways people try to take shortcuts to alleviate the pain in their life and feel better as quickly as possible? Do you think shortcuts work?

_____

_____

_____

_____

_____

_____

_____

# First Steps, Next Steps

Now it's time to get practical. We've explored many issues that prompted you to ponder and process. Let's put those thoughts into action. We'll provide several steps forward, and then it's your turn to determine three additional actions you will take this week.

1.  Chapter 3 of *Triumph over Trauma* presents four steps you can take toward healing. Which ones have you completed? Write about the experience below. And if you have yet to complete any of the Personal Healing Steps in chapter 3, commit to complete one today. Which step are you committing to complete?

    _____

    _____

    _____

    _____

    _____

2.  Have you ever judged someone who can't seem to get over a painful experience in their past? Have you ever thought to yourself, *They should be over that by now*, or *That wasn't such a big deal, why are they overreacting?* Maybe you expressed those sentiments at the time, and maybe you didn't. If you didn't, there's no need to confess them now, but consider reaching out to that person with an encouraging note, email, text, or phone call. Simply express that you know they've suffered, and they are in your thoughts.

    _____

    _____

_____

_____

_____

**3.** God restored health, wealth, and family to Job. Jesus restored life to
Lazarus and health to many who came to him for help. Some people
do not experience restoration of things lost but do experience a vibrant
new chapter of life filled with new blessings from God. Do you believe
God can bring restoration and new blessings into your life? Ask him to
begin to reveal to you the good things he has in store for you.

_____

_____

_____

_____

_____

**4.** Your turn. What additional steps do you intend to take this week to
move toward wellness?

a. _____

_____

_____

b. _____

_____

_____

c.  _____

_____

_____

## Closing Reflections

Understanding the truth about trauma—what causes it, who experiences it, what doesn't lead to recovery and what does—paves the way toward health and healing. Denial might help to avoid pain in the moment, but it doesn't get you anywhere, and believing lies that hold you back creates even more trauma. The truth, however, really can set you free.

## Scripture for Meditation

"See, I am doing a new thing! Now it springs up; do you not perceive it? I am making a way in the wilderness and streams in the wasteland."

ISAIAH 43:19

## Wise Words to Awaken Your Spirit

"Take the first step in faith. You don't have to see the whole staircase, just take the first step."

MARTIN LUTHER KING JR.

# Journal Your Journey

This week you are going to be taking steps forward, forging new habits, and letting go of old ones. Will these things make a difference? Will you be able to discern any changes in how you feel and what you think?

This page is here for you to journal about the journey. What works? What doesn't? You'll know what to keep doing because you'll have your adventure documented in the pages of this workbook. Use this space to ask questions, make lists, doodle, write about your progress, record milestones, and write your forgiveness statement(s).

Let the adventure begin!

_____

_____

_____

_____

_____

_____

_____

_____

_____

_____

_____

_____

_____

_____

_____

_____

_____

_____

_____

_____

_____

_____

_____

_____

_____

_____

_____

_____

_____

_____

_____

_____

# Restore Your Freedom

*Why Forgiveness Is Essential for Healing*

**Review chapter 10 from the *Triumph over Trauma* book**

## Week 4 at a Glance

Forgiveness is a foundational and essential practice necessary to heal whatever is causing trouble in your life. This is especially true for trauma survivors, whose pain is often caused by another person.

The thought of forgiving a perpetrator is difficult to fathom. It's so counterintuitive and goes against our internal yearning to hold the guilty accountable.

But, in one of life's strange paradoxes, a spirit of unforgiveness can harm the trauma survivor more than it harms the perpetrator. Harboring resentment and bitterness can pull you down emotionally, physically, relationally, and spiritually. Your ongoing indignation can paralyze you, dominating your thoughts. It can prevent much-needed sleep while fostering anxiety and depression. And it can hinder your friendships, either because you no longer fully trust others or because your natural guardedness causes you to withdraw.

Conversely, forgiving an offender—even an unrepentant one—makes incredible sense. And it is incredibly healing. As we forgive, we begin to rise above the hurt and injustice that have imprisoned us. Taking

41

initiative to forgive is the wise thing to do, for our own peace of mind as well as the healthy recovery of your body, soul, and spirit.

Emotional, physical, relational, and spiritual freedom cannot co-exist with resentment and unforgiveness. Therefore, to recover from trauma, overcome bitterness, and restore whole-person health, it's essential that you choose the freedom that comes from forgiving.

But forgiving someone (especially if that someone is yourself) is often easier said than done. It takes courage, maturity, and a step of faith.

## Essential Ideas . . . and Your Insights

1.  **A spirit of unforgiveness is harmful—not to the perpetrator, but to you and those you love.** When you hang on to hurt and resentment, a damaging barrage of negativity can dominate your thoughts—and your life. Researchers at the Mayo Clinic have found that if you refuse or neglect to forgive, you may bring anger and bitterness into every relationship. You may become depressed or anxious, feel that your life lacks purpose, and feel at odds with your spiritual beliefs. You may even experience diminished ability to connect meaningfully with others.[2] In counseling thousands of trauma survivors, my team and I have found that unforgiveness is likely to undermine one's physical and emotional health.

    **Your response:** In the aftermath of trauma, have you resisted the challenge to forgive? If so, what unhealthy conditions have you (or those close to you) noticed in your life such as those mentioned above? How has unforgiveness affected your overall happiness?

    _____

    _____

    _____

    _____

2. **Forgiveness is not about letting someone get away with something.**
   Many survivors of trauma suffer from the mistaken idea that to
   forgive means saying "that's okay" about behavior that clearly is not.
   The important principle here is that it's not your job to punish or
   bring the offender to justice. For your own sake—and for the sake of
   those you love—your job is to make sure your heart and your health
   are right, despite the hurt you've endured.

   **Your response:** Have you held the opinion that forgiveness would
   be like shrugging off a person's bad behavior? What, for you, should
   be involved in acknowledging the offender's harmful acts while also
   fully forgiving that person?

   _____

   _____

   _____

   _____

3. **Profound benefits and blessings are in store for you when you
   forgive.** Forgiveness is like a snowball rolling downhill: once moving,
   it keeps growing and picking up speed. With the recovering clients I
   work with, I've seen time and time again that forgiving the offender
   helps lighten their emotional load, brighten their recovery time,
   invigorate their health, and restore their positive outlook.

   **Your response:** What other benefits do you think might come
   with the act of forgiveness? How have you benefited—physically,
   emotionally, spiritually—when you found the courage to forgive
   someone?

   _____

   _____

_____

_____

_____

## Taking Stock

Forgiveness is a practical and necessary step in healing from trauma. Clinging to the hurt only deepens your feelings of anger, frustration, and resentment. Use these exercises to better understand your resistance to forgiving others and to draw strength to forgive.

I want the courage and strength to forgive (name someone) _____

for _____.

But I haven't yet let go of how he/she/they hurt me in these ways:
1.

2.

3.

4.

I fear that if I do forgive, it will . . .
1.

2.

3.

4.

Things I've learned about forgiveness that surprise me:

1.

2.

3.

4.

I hope that forgiving will benefit me in the following ways:

1.

2.

3.

4.

I'm learning that forgiveness is *not*:

1.

2.

3.

4.

Rather, forgiveness *is*:

1.

2.

3.

4.

Things I need to ask someone else's forgiveness for:

1.

2.

3.

4.

Things I've been holding against myself or against God:
1.

2.

3.

4.

Steps that will help me release past hurts, if I choose to put them to work:
1.

2.

3.

4.

## Change Your Story, Change Your Life

1. What is the story you've been telling yourself about forgiving someone who caused or contributed to your trauma? What negative self-talk has hindered you ("But I'm so deeply hurt . . . He brought such major upheaval to my life . . . I just can't forgive her . . .")? Write out your story—just let it flow without self-editing or filtering.

_____

_____

_____

_____

_____

_____

_____

_____

_____

_____

_____

_____

_____

2. Now, from what you've learned in this chapter, write out a different narrative you want to embrace. How do you want this situation to resolve? Describe your ideal life, free of bitterness or resentment. What steps are you willing to take to break free—right now?

_____

_____

_____

_____

_____

_____

_____

_____

_____

_____

# Dig Deeper

1.  After studying this chapter, what can you say are the drawbacks of not forgiving someone who has harmed you? (Think about the physical, emotional, relational, spiritual aspects.)

    _____

    _____

    _____

2.  What would you say are the benefits and blessings of forgiving the offender, regardless of whether he/she/they seem remorseful?

    _____

    _____

    _____

3.  What reasons do you tend to give yourself for reluctance to forgive someone who has caused you harm?

    _____

    _____

    _____

4.  Ephesians 4:31-2 instructs us to "get rid of all bitterness, rage, anger, harsh words . . . instead, be kind to each other, tenderhearted, forgiving one another, just as God through Christ has forgiven you" (NLT). What is your personal response to this admonition?

    _____

    _____

    _____

5. What have you found to be most helpful in this week's study? Most motivating?

_____

_____

_____

## First Steps, Next Steps

Now it's time to get practical. We've explored several issues that prompted you to ponder and process. Let's put those thoughts into action. I'll provide three steps forward, and then it's your turn to determine three other steps you will take this week.

1. Take time to review your personal history—from years ago to recently. Can you think of someone (or several people) you need to forgive? Write about any resistance you feel about forgiving. Then create a plan to follow through on what you've learned from this week's study.

_____

_____

_____

2. What misconceptions have you held regarding forgiveness that may have kept you from being willing to forgive?

_____

_____

_____

3. Write out what you might say to your offender(s) if you are given the opportunity to communicate one-on-one.

_____

_____

_____

4. Your turn. What steps do you intend to take this week to heed the scriptural imperative to forgive and move toward wholeness?

   a. _____

   _____

   _____

   _____

   b. _____

   _____

   _____

   _____

   c. _____

   _____

   _____

   _____

## Closing Reflections

If I were to distill the essence of this week's theme into an equation, it would be this:

Forgiveness = Freedom

Forgiveness is the place where you experience release and relief from your own hurtful actions and the hurtful actions of others. Without that freedom, you will continue to carry toxic emotions that contaminate your heart and corrupt your thoughts.

Scripture tells us not to stay angry or hold grudges. Why? One reason is that anger is mostly harmful to the person who is angry. Unaddressed and unreleased anger is poisonous to the body, mind, and spirit.

So why don't we let it go? Because, ironically, it feels good to be mad. Anger amps up our adrenaline and energizes our emotions. Anger gives us a sense of control and power. What's more, it's simply *easier* to nurture anger than offer forgiveness. As author Frederick Buechner says:

> Of the Seven Deadly Sins, anger is possibly the most fun. To lick your wounds, to smack your lips over grievances long past, to roll over your tongue the prospect of bitter confrontations still to come, to savor to the last toothsome morsel both the pain you are given and the pain you are giving back—in many ways it is a feast fit for a king. The chief drawback is that what you are wolfing down is yourself. The skeleton at the feast is you.[3]

Such vivid imagery conveys the destructive power of holding grudges and the need to work through the difficult process of letting them go. Personal transformation is attainable and healing from trauma is indeed achievable . . . but both depend on your willingness to forgive.

## Scripture for Meditation

"As God's chosen people, holy and dearly loved, clothe yourselves with compassion, kindness, humility, gentleness and patience. Bear with each other and forgive one another if any of you has a grievance against someone. Forgive as the Lord forgave you. And over all these virtues put on love, which binds them all together in perfect unity."

COLOSSIANS 3:12-14

## Wise Words to Awaken Your Spirit

"Forgiveness is the economy of the heart. . . . Forgiveness saves the expense of anger, the cost of hatred, the waste of spirits."

HANNAH MORE

# Journal Your Journey

This week you are going to be taking steps forward, forging new habits, and letting go of old ones. Will these things make a difference? Will you be able to discern any changes in how you feel and what you think?

This page is here for you to journal about the journey. What works? What doesn't? You'll know what to keep doing because you'll have your adventure documented in the pages of this workbook. Use this space to ask questions, make lists, doodle, write about your progress, record milestones, and write your forgiveness statement(s).

Let the adventure begin!

_____

_____

_____

_____

_____

_____

_____

_____

_____

_____

_____

_____

_____

_____

_____

_____

_____

_____

_____

_____

_____

_____

_____

_____

_____

_____

_____

_____

_____

_____

_____

# Revisit the Hurt

*Grieve Your Losses So You Can Move Beyond*

**Review chapter 11 in the *Triumph over Trauma* book**

## Week 5 at a Glance

This chapter presents a "tough love" scenario. In order to heal from painful experiences, you must be willing to look closely at what has happened and take steps to address your painful emotions.

That is tough! The process is not easy or simple. Looking at your deepest wounds is one of the hardest things you'll ever do in life.

Here is the *love* part of the "tough love" equation. When you love yourself enough to experience pain, your present life and your future life will be infinitely more free and joyful. The *tough* aspects of digging deep will enable you to *love* yourself and your life like never before. There is no getting around it: Healing comes from the grieving process.

I share with you one of my favorite Scripture passages: "Know the truth, and the truth will set you free" (John 8:32). That is profound wisdom. Confronting the truth of your past pain is mighty tough—but doing so will indeed set you free.

## Essential Ideas . . . and Your Insights

1. **Trauma has a way of burrowing deep into our brain and heart.**
   Trauma has a way of hiding in the dark places within us, away from
   the light of day. The sad fact is that many trauma survivors don't
   achieve healing because they never examine and address their source
   of trauma.

   This is an understandable "stuck point" for many people. Why
   go back and revisit the most painful moment of one's life? It's a great
   question, and a few common truths would seem to further strengthen
   the "leave your pain buried" argument:

   ☐ No one wants to experience more pain

   ☐ Human beings are designed and conditioned to avoid
   pain

   ☐ The survival of humankind depends upon avoiding
   the worst kinds of pain (e.g., fire, animal attack,
   exposure to the elements, starvation)

   **Your response:** Have you had difficulty looking at the source of
   your trauma? If so, do you know why? Since it is perfectly natural and
   understandable to want to avoid your deepest pain, what would help
   you make the step of exploring your experiences?

   _____

   _____

   _____

   _____

   _____

   _____

2.  **Courage and resilience are essential allies in your path forward.**
    For survivors of trauma, life can seem life a constant uphill climb,
    with one obstacle after another on the path toward wholeness. But
    the effort is well worth the reward.

    I want to give you a few practical reasons why revisiting your
    trauma is helpful for your healing process.

    1.  Confronting your trauma is the only way through it

    2.  Facing trauma takes courage, but not once have I seen a person
        regret the process

    3.  By working through your trauma, you will gain greater peace
        and joy

    4.  By processing trauma, you will regain power and control in
        your life

    5.  As you get healthy yourself, you can help others confront their
        own trauma and grow because of it


    In order to move into a healthier place in life, you need to face
    the experience—or several experiences—that most wounded you
    in the past. I am reminded of the Robert Frost poem "A Servant
    to Servants," where he says, "The best way out is always through."[4]
    That short line is long on wisdom. You will move out of your pain by
    working through it.

    **Your response:** Where do you draw strength and courage to press
    on through life's challenges? How can you apply the poet's wisdom to
    your situation ("the best way out is always through")?

    _____

    _____

    _____

    _____

3.  **The "Five Stages of Grief," most often applied to the loss of a loved one, apply to any kind of traumatic experience and can help us acknowledge our feelings.** Here is a brief review (with a fuller description provided in the book).

    a.  Denial. When you experience a traumatic event, your survival instincts kick in and your brain may default to fight-or-flight mode. Our first response may be to protect ourselves by denying the event.

    b.  Bargaining. This stage of grief may be marked by persistent thoughts about what could have been done to prevent the loss or trauma.

    c.  Depression. Here, we begin to realize and feel the true extent of the loss or trauma. Depression sets in when we begin to face the full brunt of the trauma we experienced.

    d.  Anger. This stage usually happens when we feel helpless and powerless. Anger can stem from a feeling of abandonment because of loss, including losses brought on by trauma.

    e.  Acceptance. This is the point where we can say, "Yes, what happened to me was unfair and terrible. However, I have come to terms with the event and processed it accordingly. As I let go of my grief and surrender control over it, I am now freed from it."

    **Your response:** The grief process is rarely linear, moving from one step to the next. You could be anywhere in this process. Do you see yourself currently in any of these stages? What rings true for you about the stages described here? Is it hard for you to image ever getting to the acceptance stage? Why or why not?

    _____

    _____

    _____

    _____

# Taking Stock

Chapter 11 of *Triumph over Trauma* presents the comparison of the ostrich and the bison as a parallel for people *who are not* and *who are* willing to address their painful experiences.

An ostrich has the reputation of putting its head in the sand to avoid danger while a bison will gather with others of their kind and run toward a storm.

These examples give us a chance to evaluate how willing or unwilling we are to explore our hurts. Answer the following questions, recognizing that there is no reason for self-criticism or self-judgment. You are simply seeking to understand where you are on your journey toward healing.

1. Are you open to looking closely at the event(s) that caused your trauma?
   _____ No way. Not going there
   _____ Possibly, under the right circumstances (such as with the guidance of a caring counselor)
   _____ Sometime in the future, but not right now
   _____ Yes, I'm all in

2. What prompted your response to the previous question?
   _____ My past experience is just too painful to revisit
   _____ I am eager to move forward with my healing, but the process stirs up a lot of pain
   _____ I'm ready to face my pain so I can move past it in order to live fully and freely
   _____ Other. Include your unique response

   _____

   _____

   _____

In chapter 11, I said, "Typically, the negative habits or behaviors that plague us are things we are already aware of but just don't want to deal with. Maybe it's because the thought of correcting negative behavior is overwhelming or exhausting."

3.  What habits or behaviors of yours might be delaying or impeding your healing process?

_____

_____

_____

_____

4.  It is important to pause every now and then while doing hard emotional work to focus on the positive. So . . . what do you like about yourself and appreciate about yourself at this point in your journey toward wholeness? Don't hold back—be kind to yourself.

_____

_____

_____

_____

## Change Your Story, Change Your Life

1.  What is the story you tell yourself and others about your traumatic experiences? Whom do you blame? A perpetrator? Yourself? God? Life circumstances? Describe how your life changed as a result of your wound. Write out your own story—just let it flow without self-editing or filtering.

_____

_____

_____

_____

2.  Now write out a different narrative that describes the healing and restoration you want to embrace. Where do you want to end up? Describe your ideal life, free of fear and pain.

_____

_____

_____

_____

## Dig Deeper

1.  Are you in the habit of framing your identity in terms of your traumatic past? How so?

_____

_____

_____

_____

_____

_____

2. How do you think that identity would be different if those painful
   events had never happened? Be specific.

   _____

   _____

   _____

   _____

3. Are you willing to believe that this alternate identity is still possible?
   Are you ready to let go of the pain you know for the chance to be that
   person now? Why or why not?

   _____

   _____

   _____

   _____

4. What does the thought of forgiving others (or yourself) for
   past wrongs make you feel? What are your reasons for avoiding
   forgiveness? What reasons can you think of to give it a try?

   _____

   _____

   _____

   _____

5. What good things are present in your life today that have nothing to do with your fear or pain? Name as many as you can think of.

_____

_____

_____

_____

# First Steps, Next Steps

Now it's time to get practical. We've explored many issues that prompted you to ponder and process. Let's put those thoughts into action. I'll provide three steps forward, and then it's your turn to determine three other steps you will take this week.

1. Spend twenty minutes writing what you believe about yourself and your future. Then read back over it looking for lies with roots in your past trauma. Pay close attention to harsh judgments and hopelessness. Are these ideas true? Are they helpful?

_____

_____

_____

_____

_____

_____

2. Break the spell of anguish over the past by breaking your routine in the moment. When familiar feelings of anxiety or depression start to appear, disrupt your coping habits by choosing something completely different. Go for a walk, call a friend, write in your journal, bake a cake. How does this change your experience of the fear?

_____

_____

_____

_____

_____

_____

3. Enlist accomplices. Rewiring your thoughts about self-care, safety, reconnection, and integration will be hard—and sometimes frightening—work. It isn't necessary to do it alone. Who would you choose to stand with you?

_____

_____

_____

_____

_____

_____

4.  Your turn. What steps do you intend to take this week to move toward wellness?

    a.  _____

        _____

        _____

    b.  _____

        _____

        _____

    c.  _____

        _____

        _____

## Closing Reflections

For many people, moving through the trauma recovery process prepares them to say, "A horrible thing happened. Without dismissing the impact of that hurt or heartache on my life, I can say that I am a stronger person as a result of what happened, I have learned how to create space and care for myself, and I am empowered and free to live a life with meaning and purpose."

Are you ready to make these your words?

## Scripture for Meditation

"He heals the brokenhearted and binds up their wounds."

PSALM 147:3

## Wise Words to Awaken Your Spirit

"Although the world is full of suffering, it is also full of the overcoming of it."

HELEN KELLER

## Journal Your Journey

This week you are going to be trying out new things, taking steps forward, forging new habits, and letting go of old ones. Will these things make a difference? Will you be able to discern any changes in how you feel and what you think?

This page is here for you to journal about the journey. What works? What doesn't? You'll know what to keep doing because you'll have your adventure documented in the pages of this workbook. Use this space to ask questions, make lists, doodle, write about your progress, and record milestones.

Let the adventure begin!

_____

_____

_____

_____

_____

_____

_____

_____

_____

_____

_____

_____

_____

_____

_____

_____

_____

_____

_____

_____

_____

_____

_____

_____

# Revitalize Your Body

*Regain Your Physical Strength and Confidence*

**Review chapter 12 from the *Triumph over Trauma* book**

## Week 6 at a Glance

Let's face it: striving to heal from trauma can be exhausting. As you try to process and overcome the hurt, disruption, and betrayal, it's highly likely that you've become tired and weary. You may have difficulty sleeping. You might not feel like eating well, opting instead for comfort foods. And exercise? Forget it. In the difficult situation you're in, exercise holds no appeal whatsoever.

Although now is when you need to be at your best, you're worn out. Emotionally, you feel disheartened and your confidence has dwindled. Mentally, you don't feel as sharp and positive as you used to. Spiritually, you may not feel like engaging in the pursuits that once brought you peace and vitality, and you might wonder why God doesn't seem to be answering your prayers.

All of these post-trauma symptoms are quite normal. Not healthy, mind you, but normal and understandable in the wake of traumatic events. Your body has a symbiotic relationship with your soul, mind, and emotions. When one dimension suffers, the others suffer. They are interdependent. If you've allowed trauma to debilitate your physical health, your soul, mind, and emotions will be weakened as well.

The good news—the healthy news—is that the reverse is also true: taking steps now to revitalize your body will also strengthen your soul, mind, and emotions. Doing so will make you far more fit to tackle and triumph over your troubles. Good physical health will sustain *the whole you* as you journey toward recovery.

## Essential Ideas ... and Your Insights

1.  **All aspects of our being—body, soul, mind, and emotions— are inextricably intertwined and affect one another every day, for better or worse.** In the aftermath of your trauma, you have likely found this to be true. When you're distressed, your heart races and your blood pressure increases. You experience tension in your stomach and notice your muscles tightening and fists clenching. Unabated, this response can eventually wear you down, give you headaches, make you feel tired, and even lead to serious illnesses.

    **Your response:** How have you been feeling lately? As your mind and emotions have suffered, in what ways has your physical health been compromised? What would you like to change about your physical condition and how you feel?

    _____

    _____

    _____

    _____

2.  **In order to rise above pain and conquer post-trauma anguish, it's essential to enhance the quality of foods (fuel) you put in your body.** God created your body to run on proper fuel. However, our culture pushes thousands of processed, pre-packaged foods bearing

long lists of ingredients that are impossible to pronounce. Then we have tempting fast-food places on every corner, offering choices that usually do little to fortify us with helpful nutrients. Whether for convenience or "comfort food," it's far too easy to consume lousy fuel when we really need to be at our best.

**Your response:** How would you classify most of the foods and beverages you've consumed recently? What have you noticed about your energy level and sense of overall vitality? How would you *like* to feel?

_____

_____

_____

_____

3. **Regular, focused physical exercise is another key to regaining physical strength and confidence.** Because of the hardships you've experienced, it's possible that you've fallen into a common trap: feeling low (or zero) motivation to exercise or engage in physical activity of any kind. The temptation is to become sedentary, sitting on the couch and watching movies. But countless studies confirm that consistent physical movement strengthens bones, fortifies muscle, reduces unhealthy fat, and re-energizes you. Regular exercise also enhances the release of essential chemicals and hormones that will help alleviate depression and calm the worrisome thoughts that have plagued you. So take to heart this helpful fact: When you least feel like exercising is the best time to get off the couch and do so. You'll notice a positive difference almost immediately.

**Your response:** As you have struggled with difficult experiences and emotions, what has been your attitude toward regular physical exercise? If you have avoided it, why? What are you willing to do to get active even when you don't feel like it?

_____

_____

_____

_____

## Taking Stock

Conscientious care for your body is integral to the health of your soul, mind, and emotions. The foods and beverages you consume, the frequency and caliber of your movement, and your quality of sleep will help or hinder your healing journey. Use the following exercises to better understand your present condition and draw inspiration to step up your physical self-care.

1.  Have your body, soul, mind, and emotions been working together to provide you energy and vitality? Or has one aspect (or more) been lagging and dragging you down?

_____

_____

_____

_____

_____

_____

2.  On a scale of 1 to 5, with 1 being very weak and 5 being strong, circle the number that best describes your present situation.

    a.  My current overall physical condition     1  2  3  4  5

    b.  How I feel physically on most days     1  2  3  4  5

    c.  The firmness of my muscles     1  2  3  4  5

    d.  The firmness of my waistline     1  2  3  4  5

    e.  The girth of my waistline     1  2  3  4  5

    f.  The nutritional quality of many foods and beverages I've been consuming     1  2  3  4  5

    g.  My discipline for regular exercise     1  2  3  4  5

    h.  My quality and quantity of restful sleep     1  2  3  4  5

    i.  My level of energy and endurance     1  2  3  4  5

    j.  My overall mood and state of mind     1  2  3  4  5

3.  From your answers above, what conclusions would you draw about your current physical condition? How do your answers make you feel?

_____

_____

_____

_____

_____

4.  Review "Essential Fuels for Your Body and Mind" in book chapter 12. What healthy foods, beverages, and supplements have you been consuming during your journey to recovery? What essential fuels have you minimized or even ignored as you have dealt with difficult experiences?

    _____

    _____

    _____

    _____

    _____

5.  Reflect on the axiom, "You are what you eat." What does this assertion mean to you personally? Are you pleased or disheartened at what it tells you about your present state?

    _____

    _____

    _____

    _____

    _____

6.  Lately, have you been telling yourself you just don't feel up to exercising? Have you been intimidated at the idea? Describe your feelings.

    _____

    _____

_____

_____

_____

7. Based on the "Get Off the Couch" section of book chapter 12, what benefits of regular exercise stand out to you the most?

_____

_____

_____

_____

_____

8. Sleep quality is another key ingredient of life quality; good sleep helps to energize your recovery while poor sleep only impedes you. When it comes to sleep habits, do you regularly . . .

a. Catch some sunlight during the day?  b. Yes / No

c. Take a nice walk or get other good exercise?  d. Yes / No

e. Limit caffeine and alcohol?  f. Yes / No

g. Grab a quick nap?  h. Yes / No

i. Follow a relaxing bedtime routine?  j. Yes / No

k. Enjoy a sleep-friendly environment?  l. Yes / No

m. Cease all electronic media an hour before bed?  n. Yes / No

9.  Did you circle one or more items in the "no" column? What do your
    answers reveal about your sleep hygiene and what you can do to
    improve your quality of sleep?

    _____

    _____

    _____

    _____

    _____


## Change Your Story, Change Your Life

1.  What stories have you been telling yourself about your present
    physical state? What self-talk may be keeping you from being at your
    best ("Comfort food will help lessen the pain . . . I don't feel like
    exercising today . . . I'll get back in shape *someday* . . . If I stay up late
    and/or take sleeping pills, I'll sleep better")? Write out your story—
    just let it flow without self-editing or filtering.

    _____

    _____

    _____

    _____

    _____

    _____

2. Now, from what you've learned in this study, write out a different narrative you want to embrace. How do you want to put your current condition behind you? Describe your ideal life, eating healthfully, staying in shape, sleeping well. What are you willing do *today* to get started toward a renewed sense of vitality?

_____

_____

_____

_____

_____

# Dig Deeper

1. After studying and reflecting on this chapter, what can you say are the drawbacks of letting your physical health and strength fall off during trauma and recovery? (Think about the mental, emotional, spiritual aspects.)

_____

_____

_____

_____

_____

_____

_____

2.  What do you now realize are the benefits (mental, emotional, spiritual)
    of taking better care your body as you work toward wholeness?

    _____

    _____

    _____

    _____

    _____

    _____

    _____


3.  If taking care of your body has been a struggle, why do you think
    it's been so hard to eat better, exercise, or get quality sleep in the
    aftermath of your trauma?

    _____

    _____

    _____

    _____

    _____

    _____

    _____

    _____

4.  What three things about your present state of physical strength and health do you most want to improve, starting today?

_____

_____

_____

_____

_____

_____

_____

5.  What have you found to be most promising and helpful about this week's study? Why?

_____

_____

_____

_____

_____

_____

_____

_____

## First Steps, Next Steps

Now it's time to get practical. We've explored several issues that prompted you to ponder and process. Let's put those thoughts into action. I'll provide three steps forward, and then it's your turn to determine three other steps you will take this week.

1. Select one recommendation from the section in chapter 12 titled "Consume Essential Fuels for Your Body and Mind" that you'll implement starting today. Then list three more positive changes you will make in your eating habits this week.

   _____

   _____

   _____

   _____

   _____

2. During a break or at lunchtime today, go for a 10-minute walk. Below, identify the physical activities you'll do each day this week to get your body moving again.

   _____

   _____

   _____

   _____

   _____

3. From your review of book chapter 12, identify two or three habits
   that may be preventing sufficient, quality sleep. What will you do,
   starting tonight, to overcome these detrimental habits?

   _____

   _____

   _____

   _____

   _____

4. Your turn. What other steps do you intend to take this week to regain
   your physical strength and confidence?

   a. _____

   _____

   _____

   b. _____

   _____

   _____

   c. _____

   _____

   _____

## Closing Reflections

You're working hard to recover from trauma and overcome the distress it brought into your life. In this week's study, you've seen that the physical-emotional connection is very real, and that you can harness it for good by revitalizing your body as a key part of your whole-person recovery.

Fuel your body with sufficient water and quality foods. Nurture your gut. Get off the couch and move. And adopt better bedtime habits for quality sleep. If you start putting these strategies to work today, and make them your new way of life from here on, you'll soon notice a positive difference. You will feel better and stronger. Your stress, anxiety, and weariness will begin to fade, replaced by a renewed sense of vitality.

## Scripture for Meditation

"Dear friend, I pray that you may enjoy good health and that all may go well with you, even as your soul is getting along well."

3 JOHN 1:2

## Wise Words to Awaken Your Spirit

"The human body is the best picture of the human soul."

TONY ROBBINS

# Journal Your Journey

This week you are going to be taking steps forward, forging new habits, and letting go of old ones. Will these things make a difference? Will you be able to discern any changes in how you feel and what you think?

This page is here for you to journal about the journey. What works? What doesn't? You'll know what to keep doing because you'll have your adventure documented in the pages of this workbook. Use this space to ask questions, list your goals, doodle, write about your progress, and record victories.

Let the adventure begin!

_____

_____

_____

_____

_____

_____

_____

_____

_____

_____

_____

_____

_____

_____

_____

_____

_____

_____

_____

_____

_____

_____

_____

_____

_____

_____

_____

_____

_____

_____

# Reset Your Brain

*Fully in Gear and Without Fear*

Review chapter 13 from the *Triumph over Trauma* book

## Week 7 at a Glance

In the wake of severe trauma, the shock and hurt you've experienced can take a serious toll—not only physically, but also mentally. You may battle self-deprecating thoughts such as, *Why did this happen to me?* Or, *I'm so stupid!* Or, *I can never show myself to these people again!*

Defeatist musings may also rumble through your mind: *I'll never recover from this!* Or, *I wish I could just move away and start over!*

Do those thoughts sound familiar? Such post-trauma thinking is indicative of mental distress, which can be as debilitating as physical, emotional, and spiritual anguish. As we have seen, your mind, body, emotions, and spirit are intertwined and interdependent. When one dimension suffers, all dimensions suffer . . . which makes healing from trauma even more challenging.

So this week's study addresses the all-important practice of getting your mind right. We'll take empowering steps to make sure that your brain is fully functioning per God's magnificent design—that it is working *for* you instead of against you. I'll show you how to implement two overarching strategies: (1) actively fortifying your brain—the organ that manages mind and body—to overcome the distress and anxiety that plague you; and (2) consciously turning despondent thoughts into upbeat, confident thoughts.

This deliberate "brain reset" will help relieve the cognitive upheaval you've been battling—and empower you to foster the emotional freedom you're longing for.

## Essential Ideas . . . and Your Insights

1.  **You—not your trauma—can be in control of your thoughts.** Your mind is an incredible creation. It enables you to discover creative innovations, avoid mistakes, solve problems, and make decisions that lead to a fulfilling life. But sometimes we inadvertently let our mind work against us. We live in an upside-down, inside-out world, and when cynicism and dejection abound, it's not unusual for our outlook to slip into negativity and pessimism—especially following trauma.

    When bleak thoughts come your way, you don't have to let them dominate your mindset. Martin Luther wisely observed, "You cannot keep birds from flying over your head but you can keep them from building a nest in your hair." With our Creator's help, it is within your power to take charge of your mind—to redirect and bolster your thoughts: "For God has not given us a spirit of fear, but of power and of love and of a sound mind" (2 Timothy 1:7 NKJV).

    Even in the aftermath of trauma, you can take charge of your thoughts by actively redirecting them from the negative to the positive.

    **Your response:** Have you allowed deprecating or defeatist self-talk to pull you down? How would you describe your mental strength right now? Cite an example or two. Are you ready to "get your mind right"? How do you feel about the biblical promise of 2 Timothy 1:7 quoted above?

_____

_____

_____

_____

_____

2. **Your brain requires healthy fuels to support reason, calm, confidence, and whole-person vitality.**

Just as your body needs healthy nutrition, so your brain requires essential fuels in order to bring vitality to your mind and body. This vitality (or lack thereof) happens via an amazing gut-brain connection known as the *vagus nerve.*

The vagus nerve is your body's biggest nerve, running from the brain to the gut, where it branches into a vast network of neurons known as the *gut-brain axis.* For years, scientists thought this was for the brain to more closely monitor and control digestive functions. But recent studies have shown that 90 percent of the fibers in the vagus nerve are actually sending messages *from* this intricate system of neurons in the gut *to* the brain. Some of those tiny microorganisms send messages to your brain that directly influence anxiety, depression, happiness, and satisfaction. Your vagus nerve is actually a two-way highway, with the majority of messages flowing from your gut to your brain by means of chemical messengers known as *neurotransmitters.*

Bottom line? What you feed your gut has a direct influence on the efficacy of your brain—thus on your mind and your thoughts.

So in our whole-person approach to "resetting the brain," we want to focus on the nutritional inputs that promote healthy gut bacteria and result in a better overall mood in your brain.

**Your response:** In the above paragraphs, what was new to you? How might this knowledge help explain some of the negative thoughts you been battling? What gives you a reason for hope?

_____

_____

_____

_____

3. **Four major chemical messengers (neurotransmitters) regulate your mood and the thoughts that are generated by your mood.** Your brain requires proper nutrients each day to maintain four major neurotransmitters that regulate your mood and the thoughts that result from your mood:

☐ *Serotonin* is associated with the regulation of anxiety and depression

☐ *GABA* helps balance excitement or agitation with feelings of calm

☐ *Dopamine* is associated with the "pleasure system" of the brain, providing feelings of enjoyment and reinforcement for what we're doing

☐ *Norepinephrine* involves the reactions of your brain and body to stress, including your heart rate and blood pressure

Any imbalance between these and other neurotransmitters can lead to health problems, including persistent anxiety, depression, brain fog, jitteriness, sluggishness, and insomnia. Fortunately, for each neurotransmitter that is out of balance, natural remedies such as vitamins, minerals, and amino acids can help restore proper balance. These give your brain and body the nutritional benefits needed to help relieve negativity and keep you strong physically, mentally, and emotionally.

You can help prevent or counteract neurotransmitter imbalances by following the nutritional advice in chapter 12—including the daily use of a good multivitamin/mineral/amino-acid supplement. This may be all you need. If you wish to explore further supplementation, review the section in chapter 13 titled "Soothing Substances for Brain Health."

**Your response:** As you read about neurotransmitters (chemical messengers) and how the gut-brain axis works, what did the "two-way highway" reveal to you about your gut's influence on your brain? On your moods and thoughts?

_____

_____

_____

_____

## Taking Stock

In chapter 13, we've seen how to "reset your brain" by implementing two overarching strategies: (1) fortifying your brain biologically through good nutrition, and (2) consciously turning despondent thoughts into upbeat, confident thoughts. The following exercises will help you better understand your present state and begin a powerful reset toward healing and hope.

I am tired of feeling _____. I'm ready to change my mindset from _____ to optimism and hope for the future.

But I'm afraid that I've allowed the following factors to prevent me from taking charge of my thoughts:

1.

2.

3.

4.

In the aftermath of my trauma, I've let my moods and thoughts pull me down because:

1.

2.

3.

4.

Learning about the gut-brain axis and the importance of proper nourishment has taught me that _____

_____

_____


The foods and beverages I've been consuming meet the recommendations given in chapter 12. Yes or no? How might you improve in this area?

_____

_____

_____

According to Proverbs 23:7, as I think within myself, so I am. The bulk of my post-tramatic thought life can be described this way: _____

_____

_____

Of the prescribed steps for shifting negative thoughts to positive ones, rate yourself from 1 to 5 (1 being weak and 5 being strong):

☐ stopping negative thoughts in their tracks      1 2 3 4 5

☐ remembering the good in your life      1 2 3 4 5

☐ reframing obstacles with optimism      1 2 3 4 5

☐ talking kindly to yourself      1 2 3 4 5

What do your answers tell you? _____

_____

_____

If you were to begin taking one of these steps today, which would you select and why? _____

_____

_____

_____

_____

My favorite part of this week's study has been _____

because _____

_____

_____

## Change Your Story, Change Your Life

1.  What is the story you've been telling yourself about letting circum-
    stances control your thoughts? What kinds of brain malnourishment
    or negative self-talk have hindered your healing? Write out your
    story—just let it flow without self-editing or filtering.

    _____

    _____

    _____

    _____

    _____

    _____

    _____

    _____

    _____

    _____

2. Now, from what you've learned in chapter 13 and this week's study, write out a different narrative you want to embrace. How do you want your mental outlook to be stronger in the near future? Describe your ideal life, free of distrust, fear, and other debilitating thoughts.

_____

_____

_____

_____

_____

_____

_____

_____

_____

## Dig Deeper

1. What can you now cite as plausible reasons why you may not have been at your mental and emotional best recently?

_____

_____

_____

_____

2. How has feeling mentally/emotionally sub-par affected your post-trauma days and nights? (Think about the physical, emotional, relational, and spiritual aspects.)

_____

_____

_____

_____

_____

3. The apostle Paul told us, "Finally, brothers and sisters, whatever is true, whatever is noble, whatever is right, whatever is pure, whatever is lovely, whatever is admirable—if anything is excellent or praiseworthy—think about such things" (Philippians 4:8). What does this promise mean to you personally? How do you apply these words to your current situation?

_____

_____

_____

_____

_____

4. Based on what you've learned, what will you do, starting today, to begin getting your mind right for a stronger recovery?

_____

_____

_____

_____

_____

5. What did you find most surprising about this week's study? Most helpful? Explain.

_____

_____

_____

_____

_____

## First Steps, Next Steps

Now it's time to get practical. We've explored several issues to help you reset your brain to a more positive outlook. Let's put those thoughts into action. I'll provide three steps forward, and then it's your turn to determine three additional steps you will take this week.

1. Take another look at the foods and beverages you're consuming, along with any multivitamins and supplements you may or may not be using. Nourish your brain by initiating any needed upgrades to help ensure a healthy gut-brain axis. What changes will you make this week?

_____

_____

_____

_____

_____

2. Choose one of the "thinking good" steps to help brighten your outlook each day. Which will you review and practice this week?

_____

_____

_____

_____

_____

3. To disperse the dark emotional clouds that may hover over you, consciously look for the blessings all around you. God is indeed blessing you amid your pain, so open your eyes and notice the good that surrounds you. Big blessings, little blessings—what are they? Jot some down here.

_____

_____

_____

_____

_____

**4.** Your turn. What additional steps do you want to take this week to reset your brain and enrich your thought life?

a. _____

_____

_____

b. _____

_____

_____

c. _____

_____

_____

_____

## Closing Reflections

You have the power and ability to take charge of your thoughts instead of letting them control you. Your brain deserves healthy nourishment. Your soul deserves the peace that comes from uplifting thoughts. So in this week's study you've received proven tools to help fortify your brain and become intentional about "thinking good." As you put these ideas to work, I'm confident that the heartache of your trauma will begin to fade . . . and your future will look better and brighter.

## Scripture for Meditation

"Do not conform to the pattern of this world, but be transformed by the renewing of your mind. Then you will be able to test and approve what God's will is—his good, pleasing and perfect will."

ROMANS 12:2

## Wise Words to Awaken Your Spirit

"Keep your face always toward the sunshine—and shadows will fall behind you."

WALT WHITMAN

## Journal Your Journey

This week you are going to be taking some positive steps forward, forging new habits, and releasing old ones. Will these steps make a difference? Will you be able to discern positive changes in how you feel and what you think?

This page is here for you to journal about the journey. What works? What doesn't? You'll know what to keep doing because you'll have your adventure documented in the pages of this workbook. Use this space to ask questions, set goals, write about your progress, and record milestones.

Let the adventure begin!

_____

_____

_____

_____

_____

_____

_____

_____

_____

_____

_____

_____

_____

_____

_____

_____

_____

_____

_____

_____

_____

_____

# Reconnect with People

*Learn to Trust Those Who Are Trustworthy*

**Review chapter 14 from the *Triumph over Trauma* book**

## Week 8 at a Glance

Trauma of any kind can have a devastating effect on the survivor's present and future relationships. A key component of healthy relationships is *trust*, and when one experiences the trauma of abuse, assault, bullying, or rejection, she may find it more difficult to trust others—even those she has trusted in the past. As the soul-ache lingers, she may hesitate to draw close to others for fear of being hurt again.

While such guardedness can be helpful to one's recovery and future safety, the person can become so overcautious that it obstructs healing and healthy relationships. In addition, "triggers" (sights, sounds, smells, or someone's mannerisms) can surface unexpectedly, in otherwise benign situations, causing transference of emotional pain from past to your present.

Guardedness and triggers may cause you to isolate yourself in a self-protective cocoon, fearful of what additional traumas people might bring your way. But, ironically, this is when you need people the most—caring, kind, trustworthy people. You need them to listen, support, and encourage. And you need them to help you rediscover the faith in people you once had.

Thus it is vital to your healing that you dismantle any emotional defenses you've constructed around you. You must *decide* to rid your heart and soul of any shame, fear, resentment, or rejection you've been harboring and summon the courage to reach out and nurture a friendship or two with someone you can count on.

You need and deserve such friends.

You need and deserve to trust again.

## Essential Ideas . . . and Your Insights

1. **The sense of "guardedness" you feel can be both helpful and unhelpful.** In the aftermath of trauma, it is fully normal for the survivor to relive the unfortunate event over and over, each time experiencing the physical and emotional discomfort anew. Such introspection can grind away at one's personal confidence and trust.

   It may be small consolation, but the guardedness that results from trauma can actually be helpful to one's recovery and future safety. But if you let it, guardedness can become extreme, to the point of becoming overcautious and reluctant to trust others.

   **Your response:** Has your trauma made you more physically or emotionally "guarded" than you used to be? In what ways? Has your caution been healthy or unhealthy? Give some examples.

   _____

   _____

   _____

   _____

2. **Trauma can cause you to construct powerful emotional defense mechanisms, blocking you from learning to trust again.** It's possible that you've found yourself withdrawing or withholding from others

in fear that they may not understand or want to walk alongside you in your struggle for healing. Perhaps you've built up emotional defenses in order to keep others from turning away, distancing themselves, or hurting you again.

Ironically, the days, weeks, and months following severe trauma are when you most need a good friend, but it's also the time when you may not have sufficient confidence to reach out and trust anyone. These defenses can shrivel you inward so strongly that you can't muster the freedom or courage to share yourself with anyone.

**Your response:** Have you allowed shame or embarrassment to dominate your perspective? Have you avoided candor or fellowship with others for fear of being met with indifference? Be honest with yourself and identify one or more emotional defenses that may be hindering your relationships and trust.

_____

_____

_____

_____

3.  **In your journey of trauma recovery, you need to reconnect with people—caring people you can trust.** What you need today is a true friend, one who is supportive, empathetic, and nurturing. You need someone who stands by you no matter what—and is ready and willing to listen to you, pray for you, and affirm you as you work through your recovery. The old-time newspaper columnist Walter Winchell said it well: "A real friend is one who walks in when the rest of the world walks out." That's the kind of friend you need right now.

    You may find just one, or maybe several. You may already know that person or persons. It could be your spouse or dating partner, a trusted sibling, or a best friend who has stood beside you, holding your hand. Maybe there's another person in your life who has shown interest in getting better acquainted.

**Your response:** Have you allowed emotional defenses to turn you inward so strongly that you can't muster the courage to share yourself with others? What friend or family member(s) do you feel drawn to reconnect with on your journey to wholeness?

_____

_____

_____

_____

## Taking Stock

Learning to trust again is a practical and necessary step in healing from trauma. As someone has aptly stated, "Never be a prisoner of your past. It was a lesson, not a life sentence." Use the following exercises to better understand your situation and begin breaking free from the "prison" of distrust that may obstruct you from connecting with people.

1. Circle your answers to the following statements.
   a. My trauma was a betrayal of trust by another person. Yes / No
   b. At least one friend or family member has seemed indifferent to what I've revealed about my trauma. Yes / No
   c. In the wake of this trauma, my self-confidence has weakened. Yes / No
   d. I have felt reluctant to be candid with others about my trauma. Yes / No

e. Since my traumatic event, I have tended to withdraw from people. Yes / No

f. I don't think I trust others as much as I did prior to my trauma. Yes / No

2. What did your responses above reveal to you about your present emotional and mental state?

_____

_____

_____

_____

3. Ask yourself five questions that help post-trauma clients realize whether they have put up relational defenses:

a. Do I have the temptation to hunker down and handle it myself? Yes / No

b. Do I feel nobody will get it? Yes / No

c. Do I feel ashamed or weak—like I don't deserve support or compassion? Yes / No

d. Is there a self-protector part inside me who says: "I'm going to withdraw and stay safe so you don't hurt me"? Yes / No

e. Do I feel like I'm supposed to just deal with it myself? Yes / No

4. If you answered yes to one or more questions, it's likely that you have constructed emotional defenses to protect yourself. What specifically did you learn about yourself from your answers to these questions?

_____

_____

_____

_____

5. It's also possible that you've felt "triggered" by otherwise innocent sights, sounds, phrases, or someone's mannerisms—things that bring on a sudden, upsetting emotional remembrance of your original trauma.

   a. I've experienced a recent, unpleasant "trigger" that reminded me of my traumatic event. Yes / No

   b. If yes, this trigger(s) made me feel

_____

_____

_____

_____

   c. If no, what type of sight, sound, phrase, or demeanor *might* trigger an unexpected emotional memory in the future?

_____

_____

_____

_____

6.  I have at least one good friend who is supportive, empathetic, and nurturing. Yes / No

7.  I really *need* a true friend (or an additional good friend) right now. Yes / No

8.  The main reason I'm hesitant to trust again is _____

    _____

    _____

9.  But the main reason(s) I need to learn to trust again include:
    a.
    b.
    c.
    d.

10. The component of healthy relationships outlined in this chapter that stands out to me the most is _____

    because _____

    _____

    _____

## Change Your Story, Change Your Life

1.  What is the story you've been telling yourself about holding back from others following your trauma? What negative self-talk has hindered your connection with people ("I don't know if I can trust her . . . I

need to be careful something like this doesn't happen again . . . He may tell others my secret struggles . . . She may not be interested in my situation . . . I may be betrayed again . . .")? Write out your story— just let it flow without self-editing or filtering.

_____

_____

_____

_____

2. Now, from what you've learned in chapter 14 of the book and this week's study, write out a different narrative you want to embrace. How do you want your reluctance to resolve? Describe your ideal life, free of distrust or fear.

_____

_____

_____

_____

## Dig Deeper

1. What can you now say are the drawbacks of not trusting someone who may be willing to be supportive? (Think about the physical, emotional, relational, and spiritual aspects.)

_____

_____

_____

_____

2.  What would you say are the benefits of learning to reconnect with and trust others again?

_____

_____

_____

_____

3.  Ask God to help you identify someone you may already feel connected with, who may be willing to listen to you and support your journey to triumph over trauma. Write that person's name here and say why you think he or she could be a good, true friend for you during this time.

_____

_____

_____

_____

4.  What will you do, starting today, to begin dropping any undue defenses you've built up—and become more transparent with this friend or family member?

_____

_____

_____

_____

5.  What have you found to be most surprising in this week's study?
    Most helpful?

    _____

    _____

    _____

    _____

## First Steps, Next Steps

Now it's time to get practical. We've explored several issues that prompted
you to ponder and process. Let's put those thoughts into action. I'll
provide three steps forward, and then it's your turn to determine three
additional steps you will take this week.

1.  A proverb tells us, "Friends love through all kinds of weather,
    and families stick together in all kinds of trouble" (17:17 MSG).
    Contemplate what this means for you, in your situation. How will
    living by this statement help elevate your confidence and your
    healing?

    _____

    _____

    _____

    _____

2. Begin dismantling those emotional defenses today, including any triggers that may have troubled you. Starting now, claim the admonition and promise of 1 Peter 5:7: "Give all your worries and cares to God, for he cares about you" (NLT). You may need to do this, in prayer, each day over several days or weeks. By faith, be confident that your defense mechanisms are no longer needed.

   _____

   _____

   _____

   _____

3. Review the "Seven Components of Healthy Relationships" described in this chapter. Then summon your courage and reach out to the person you identified above as a potential true friend you can count on. Who is this person, and can you name more than one?

   _____

   _____

   _____

   _____

4. Your turn. What additional steps do you want to take this week to begin trusting others again and reconnecting with trustworthy people?

   a. _____

   _____

   _____

b. _____

_____

_____


c. _____

_____

_____


## Closing Reflections

All of us need good people in our lives—loving, supportive people we can trust. And in the weeks, months, and years following personal trauma, having such friends and family members is essential to healing and recovery.

Sadly, it's important to realize that some friends may not be able to handle what you're going through. They may subtly withdraw because they don't know what to say or how to help. If you sense that a friend has become indifferent, distant, or critical, don't push. Forgive, back away for now, and refocus.

A true friend will support you in your commitment to overcome fear and learn to trust again. Among your acquaintances or perhaps among a support group is a trustworthy friend who will stand by you no matter what—and who is willing to listen to you, affirm you, and pray for you as you work through your recovery. By dismantling your defenses and reaching out, you can find and nurture a healthy, healing relationship to help nourish and strengthen you for the journey.

## Scripture for Meditation

"As iron sharpens iron, so one person sharpens another."

PROVERBS 27:17

## Wise Words to Awaken Your Spirit

"A friend is a gift you give yourself."

ROBERT LOUIS STEVENSON

## Journal Your Journey

This week you are going to be taking some positive steps forward, forging new habits, and letting go of old ones. Will these things make a difference? Will you be able to discern any changes in how you feel and what you think?

This page is here for you to journal about the journey. What works? What doesn't? You'll know what to keep doing because you'll have your adventure documented in the pages of this workbook. Use this space to ask questions, make lists, doodle, write about your progress, record milestones, and write about your intention to pursue trustworthy relationships.

Let the adventure begin!

_____

_____

_____

_____

_____

_____

_____

_____

_____

_____

_____

_____

_____

_____

_____

_____

_____

_____

_____

_____

_____

_____

_____

# Revise Your Script

*Update Your Life Narrative Based on Fact, Not Fiction*

**Review chapter 15 in the *Triumph over Trauma* book**

## Week 9 at a Glance

Like an actor interpreting a character or a director interpreting a scene, all people make interpretations about important life experiences. We assign meaning and significance to the scenes or plot points in our lives.

At times, the narrative we have written for ourselves is either flawed or downright false. At best, when we have a skewed view of our past, it inhibits our ability to accurately understand why certain things might trigger us or upset us. A flawed or false recollection of one's past can wreak havoc on a person's ability to cope with the present or possess hope for the future.

The question then becomes: How can you reassess the trauma you experienced in the light of reality and process it in such a way that you achieve a different result for a more healthy future? A major part of moving past trauma involves accurately viewing the original event and successfully readjusting your thinking about that narrative.

I use the word *narrative* pointedly because your trauma really is a story. And just as in a novel or film, the main story can be based on actual events or it can be based on fiction. In short, the story you tell yourself about the painful experiences in your life and yourself in their aftermath makes all the difference in your ability to move forward with hopefulness or stay stuck in your pain.

## Essential Ideas . . . and Your Insights

1.  **Keep your story plot moving forward.** Your trauma has the power to keep you locked in the past if you allow it to. Contrary to what your existing narrative may be telling you, your chances at peace and joy in life have not passed you by. The story you have lived until now can be rewritten.

    **Your response:** What regrets or losses have you suffered that keep you stuck in the past? Write them out and think and pray about ways to let them go—put them in the past, where they belong. I love the Old Testament passage where David says that God has cast our transgressions "as far as the east is from the west" (Psalm 103:12). What does this passage mean to you as you seek healing and wholeness?

    _____

    _____

    _____

    _____

2.  **Rewrite yourself as the main character.** Particularly if you were the survivor in your trauma history, feelings of hopelessness and helplessness may be recurring subplots in your history. Endeavor to place yourself in the middle of your narrative.

    **Your response:** Take time to write out what life looks like with you in the driver's seat, as the person who is in control now. Where will you go? What will you do? You do not need to be wealthy or powerful to take back the power in your life. You merely need to have the will to seek the help you need to get there.

_____

_____

_____

_____

_____

_____

3.  **Enlist the help of a script doctor.** Virtually every great screenplay enlists the help of others to bring the final draft into existence. As you embark on rewriting your story with yourself as the main character, seek the help of others. At minimum, build a safe circle of trusted friends and loved ones who can give you encouragement, feedback, and objective input.

    **Your response:** Think of people in your life right now who you trust and count on for support. List them here and write a few words about why these people can help you heal and move forward.

_____

_____

_____

_____

_____

# Taking Stock

As with all wounds, ignoring past trauma is an effective way to prolong the pain and loss. Use the following questions to help bring the past into the light — so the healing can begin.

I deserve to feel safe again because:
1.

2.

3.

4.

To flee from my pain, I have allowed the following destructive behaviors to grow:
1.

2.

3.

4.

I deserve to be well and free of anxiety because:
1.

2.

3.

4.

What happened to me in the past left me feeling:
1.

2.

3.

4.

Four things in my present life I can be grateful for are:
1.

2.

3.

4.

Things I look forward to having or doing again:
1.

2.

3.

4.

Remembering and mourning my wound now makes me feel:
1.

2.

3.

4.

Four healthy ways to deal with my pain:
1.

2.

3.

4.

Who I want to be now, once my past trauma becomes only *part* of my story:

1.

2.

3.

4.

## Change Your Story, Change Your Life

1. What is the story you tell yourself and others about your traumatic experiences? Whom do you blame? A perpetrator? Yourself? God? Describe how your life changed as a result of your wound. Write out your story—just let it flow without self-editing or filtering.

   _____

   _____

   _____

   _____

   _____

   _____

   _____

   _____

   _____

2. Now write out a different narrative that describes the healing and restoration you want to embrace. Where do you want to end up? Describe your ideal life, free of fear and pain.

_____

_____

_____

_____

_____

_____

_____

_____

_____

## Dig Deeper

1. Are you in the habit of framing your identity in terms of your traumatic past? How so?

_____

_____

_____

_____

_____

2. How do you think that identity would be different if those painful events had never happened? Be specific.

_____

_____

_____

_____

_____

3. Are you willing to believe that this alternate identity is still possible? Are you ready to let go of the pain you know for the chance to be that person now? Why or why not?

_____

_____

_____

_____

_____

4. How does the thought of forgiving others (or yourself) for past wrongs make you feel? What are your reasons for avoiding forgiveness? What reasons can you think of to give it a try?

_____

_____

_____

_____

_____

5.  What good things are present in your life today that have nothing to
    do with your fear or pain? Name as many as you can think of.

_____

_____

_____

_____

_____

# First Steps, Next Steps

Now it's time to get practical. We've explored many issues that prompted
you to ponder and process. Let's put those thoughts into action. We'll
provide three steps forward, and then it's your turn to determine three
other steps you will take this week.

1.  Spend twenty minutes writing what you believe about yourself and
    your future. Then read back over it looking for lies with roots in your
    past trauma. Pay close attention to harsh judgments and hopelessness.
    Are these ideas true? Are they helpful?

_____

_____

_____

_____

_____

_____

2. Break the spell of anguish over the past by breaking your routine in the moment. When familiar feelings of remorse or regret start to appear, disrupt your coping habits by choosing something completely different. Go for a walk, call a friend, write in your journal, bake a cake. How does this change your experience of the fear?

_____

_____

_____

_____

_____

_____

3. Enlist allies. Rewriting your script and identifying the truth about your past and present can be hard work. It isn't necessary to do it alone. Who would you choose to stand with you?

_____

_____

_____

_____

_____

_____

_____

4. Your turn. What steps do you intend to take this week to move toward wellness?

a. _____

_____

_____


b. _____

_____

_____


c. _____

_____

_____

## Closing Reflections

In my own journey to craft my story, my main "script doctor" has been God. Through my passionate pursuit of his will in my life, I've found the perfect director who knows me more intimately than anyone else and who is ever faithful and forgiving when I need direction.

Whatever faith background you come from, or even if you've walked away from a spiritual faith, I encourage you to seek spiritual direction and definition at this stage of your journey. You don't have to be religious to find great solace and fulfillment in spiritual enrichment.

## Scripture for Meditation

"You saw me before I was born. Every day of my life was recorded in your book. Every moment was laid out before a single day had passed."

PSALM 139:16

## Wise Words to Awaken Your Spirit

"To live by grace means to acknowledge my whole life story, the light side and the dark. In admitting my shadow side I learn who I am and what God's grace means."

BRENNAN MANNING

# Journal Your Journey

This week you are going to be trying out new things, taking steps forward, forging new habits, and letting go of old ones. Will these things make a difference? Will you be able to discern any changes in how you feel and what you think?

This page is here for you to journal about the journey. What works? What doesn't? You'll know what to keep doing because you'll have your adventure documented in the pages of this workbook. Use this space to ask questions, make lists, doodle, write about your progress, and record milestones.

Let the adventure begin!

_____

_____

_____

_____

_____

_____

_____

_____

_____

_____

_____

_____

_____

_____

_____

_____

_____

_____

_____

_____

_____

_____

_____

_____

_____

_____

_____

_____

_____

# Reclaim Your Power

*Your Strength and Resilience Are More Than Enough*

**Review chapter 16 from the *Triumph over Trauma* book**

## Week 10 at a Glance

One of the keys to achieving wholeness after trauma is believing that you can be better, stronger, and wiser because of your experiences. You don't need to stay stuck; you can grow and flourish because of the pain you endured.

Mental health professionals have given this concept a name: post-traumatic growth (PTG).

The concept first began to gain traction within mental health circles in the 1990s through research by psychologists Richard Tedeschi and Lawrence Calhoun. According to *Psychology Today*, "Post-traumatic growth is the positive psychological change that some individuals experience after a life crisis or traumatic event. Post-traumatic growth doesn't deny deep distress, but rather posits that adversity can unintentionally yield changes in understanding oneself, others, and the world. Post-traumatic growth can, in fact, coexist with post-traumatic stress disorder."[5]

Distress and PTG can happen simultaneously in those who have been traumatized. PTG is not just about survival. Neither is it simply returning to pre-trauma levels of functionality or "normalcy." PTG is about taking positive growth steps in the midst of pain, even beyond where you were before your life-altering experience. PTG is about both process and outcome.[6]

Trauma is painful in the moment, and its effects often linger for a long time. In many cases, the trauma can feel utterly pointless. But you can emerge a better, healthier person.

## Essential Ideas . . . and Your Insights

1. **Move beyond viewing yourself as a victim.** A traumatic life event might have victimized you, but the longer you view yourself as solely a victim, the longer it will take to heal. Remaining in victim mode is a dangerous place, leaving your growth stagnant at best or regressive at worst. It can create within you a troublesome emotional whirlpool that constantly tries to drag you down and create more problems.

   It's healthy and appropriate to acknowledge that you have suffered significant adversity, but don't let that status define you. Remember, you are a person of great worth and value, and you have much to offer the world.

   **Your response:** As you think about the hardship you have experienced, how do you view yourself? A "victim," a "survivor," a "child of God," a "strong person who endured," or some other phrase? How can you view yourself in a way that will empower your healing and positive journey forward?

   _____

   _____

   _____

   _____

   _____

2. **Confront and conquer false guilt.** Trauma survivors sometimes blame themselves for a painful experience even if they were not at fault. It colors the way they look at themselves and others. False guilt is also closely linked to a fear of disapproval from others. It particularly preys on people with an overly sensitive conscience, tricking them into questioning their motives and mentally chastising themselves for something they didn't do.

On the other hand, healthy guilt that occurs after we've truly erred helps us ask forgiveness from those we've hurt, repair what might be broken, set boundaries, and plot a better course for the future. Apart from healthy guilt, we would hurt others without remorse and devolve into a tragic state.

**Your response:** How do we tell the difference between false guilt and healthy guilt? One way is simply to ask ourselves, "Is there a legitimate reason that I'm feeling guilty about this situation, or am I believing lies?" Be truly honest with yourself, and the answer should reveal itself. Take time to write about any feelings of guilt you might be experiencing. Can you determine if it is false guilt that you can let go of, or justified guilt that you can act on and correct? (You might need a trusted counselor to help you discover the truth about feelings of guilt.)

_____

_____

_____

_____

_____

_____

3. **Find strength in service to others.** Focusing on others is an excellent way to bounce back from a negative life event. Serving someone else not only shifts the focus away from you and your problems, but it can also provide a deep feeling of satisfaction as you make a positive impact in the world.

   Serving others gets at the core of who we were meant to be as human beings. God created us to love him and love others. Love is sacrificial. To love is to lay down one's desires for the good of someone else.

   Even if you've never stepped foot inside a church, you've surely heard of the Golden Rule: "Do to others as you would have them do to you" (Luke 6:31). Likewise, Philippians 2:3–4 says, "Do nothing out of selfish ambition or vain conceit. Rather, in humility value others above yourselves, not looking to your own interests but each of you to the interests of the others." Whether you're religious or not, that's just good practice.

   **Your response:** There are plenty of ways to serve others all around us. Volunteer at a homeless shelter, animal shelter, or children's organization. Look on your local community website for a charity to get involved with or other ways you can give back. No matter who you are, you have been blessed with various skills. So use them to bless others. Are you good at music? Art? Cooking? Needlework? Accounting? Decorating? Graphic design? Fixing things? Whatever it is, use your talents and interests to help someone else. In what ways can you begin to serve others? What do you hope to gain from doing so?

   _____

   _____

   _____

   _____

# Taking Stock

Traumatic experiences often leave survivors feeling fearful, depressed, anxious, and unsure of themselves. That is natural and understandable. Thankfully, those unhelpful emotions can be turned into helpful, healthy emotions. Use the following questions to examine your feelings more closely — and begin to turn them toward the positive.

I would describe my current emotional state with the following words:
1.

2.

3.

4.

Knowing that no one feels emotionally strong all of the time, I would like to feel the following emotions most of the time:
1.

2.

3.

4.

I feel fearful or anxious in these situations:
1.

2.

3.

4.

When I'm feeling unsure of myself or lacking in confidence, I can use these self-talk statements to turn my thoughts about myself toward the positive:
1.

2.

3.

4.

A few strategies I can use to strengthen my self-esteem include (for ideas, review the "Bolster Your Self-Esteem" section in chapter 16):
1.

2.

3.

4.

My feelings of self-doubt and lack of confidence hold me back in these ways:
1.

2.

3.

4.

What I will gain if I achieve a healthy perspective of myself and mostly experience positive emotions:
1.

2.

3.

4.

Four courageous *actions* I could take to assert power this week:

1.

2.

3.

4.

If I didn't feel a lack of confidence and power, I would:

1.

2.

3.

4.

## Change Your Story, Change Your Life

What is the story you tell yourself about feeling a lack of power and strength? How have your trauma experiences affected your sense of resilience and self-esteem? Describe some experiences when your fear caused you to miss out on something important. Write out your story—just let it flow without self-editing or filtering.

_____

_____

_____

_____

_____

_____

Now write out a different narrative you want to embrace. Where do you want to end up? Describe your ideal life, free of fear.

_____

_____

_____

_____

_____

_____

## Dig Deeper

1.  Chapter 16 of the *Triumph over Trauma* book focuses on your self-esteem and how you view yourself. What words would you use to describe yourself currently?

_____

_____

_____

_____

_____

2.  What has been your most significant challenge related to your trauma experiences? This might be a practical issue (work productivity, attending to household tasks), an emotional issue (feeling misunderstood by others, struggling with self-esteem), or a spiritual issue (wondering where God is amid your painful experience).

_____

_____

_____

_____

_____

3. One suggestion for bolstering your self-esteem included in this chapter is "See Yourself as God Sees You." How do you believe God sees you? How does this differ from the way you see yourself?

_____

_____

_____

_____

_____

4. Another idea presented in this chapter is to "Create a Healthy Environment." What would a "healthy environment" mean for you? What can you do to make your life more healthy?

_____

_____

_____

_____

_____

5.  How do your spiritual beliefs intersect with your current struggles?
    For example, do you feel the need to "have it all together" with your
    faith-oriented friends? Do you think you should just have "more
    faith" to prevail over your problems? Or perhaps you rely on your
    spirituality as a source of strength.

    _____

    _____

    _____

    _____

    _____

## First Steps, Next Steps

Now it's time to get practical. We've explored many issues that prompted
you to ponder and process. Let's put those thoughts into action. I will
provide three steps forward, and then it's your turn to determine three
other steps you will take this week.

1.  A strategy presented in this chapter is, "Engage with life in ways
    that leave you feeling empowered." We're all familiar with the phrase
    "play to your strengths." This simply means focusing on things you're
    already good at to achieve and continue success. What are you good
    at? What activities leave you feeling empowered?

    _____

    _____

    _____

    _____

2.  Revisit a time when you felt like you couldn't do something—but you did. What caused your initial fear and hesitance? What caused you to prevail over your fear?

    _____

    _____

    _____

    _____

3.  Write a note to yourself, describing how you would ideally like to handle your fear in the future.

    _____

    _____

    _____

    _____

4.  Your turn. What steps do you intend to take this week to move toward wellness?

    a.  _____

        _____

        _____

    b.  _____

        _____

        _____

c. _____

_____

_____

## Closing Reflections

Whether you realize it or not, you are a beloved child of God. He made you uniquely in his image (Genesis 1:26–27). That means that unlike the rest of creation, you are like him in many ways.

You have the ability to love and to desire meaningful relationships, just like God.

You have creative capacity, just like God.

You have the ability to communicate and express emotions and feelings, just like God.

You are glad when good things happen and desire justice when you see evil and unfairness, just like God.

Lamentations 3:19–23 provides a wonderful reminder and encouragement of how God sees you in the midst of your grief: "I remember my affliction and my wandering, the bitterness and the gall. I well remember them, and my soul is downcast within me. Yet this I call to mind and therefore I have hope: Because of the LORD's great love we are not consumed, for his compassions never fail. They are new every morning; great is your faithfulness."

## Scripture for Meditation

"Consider it pure joy, my brothers and sisters, whenever you face trials of many kinds, because you know that the testing of your faith produces perseverance. Let perseverance finish its work so that you may be mature and complete, not lacking anything."

JAMES 1:2–4

# Wise Words to Awaken Your Spirit

"The most beautiful people we have known are those who have known defeat, known suffering, known struggle, known loss, and have found their way out of the depths. These persons have an appreciation, a sensitivity and an understanding of life that fills them with compassions, gentleness, and a deep loving concern. Beautiful people do not just happen."

ELIZABETH KUBLER-ROSS

# Journal Your Journey

This week you are going to be trying out new things, taking steps forward, forging new habits, and letting go of old ones. Will these things make a difference? Will you be able to discern any changes in how you feel and what you think?

This page is here for you to journal about the journey. What works? What doesn't? You'll know what to keep doing because you'll have your adventure documented in the pages of this workbook. Use this space to ask questions, make lists, doodle, write about your progress, and record milestones.

Let the adventure begin!

_____

_____

_____

_____

_____

_____

_____

_____

_____

_____

_____

_____

_____

_____

_____

_____

_____

_____

_____

_____

_____

_____

_____

_____

# Reinforce Your Spirituality

*Tap into God's Healing Power*

**Review chapter 17 from the *Triumph over Trauma* book**

## Week 11 at a Glance

In order to experience genuine healing, we must recognize any dead ends we're in and rejoin the path toward wholeness. Along this path, we walk in relationship with God.

In a world of broken connections, God's promise of friendship binds us to him. In a world of unsteady relationships, God's steadfast love keeps us on firm ground. In a world of goodbyes, God's presence is a continual "I am with you always."

God accepts and shapes us even when our relationships with others are broken. God doesn't deny the sorrow that comes when death, separation, and loss occur. Rather, he acknowledges the reality of the new shape and works within us to make us whole. There is no need for an external patch, as if somehow you are defective after you've suffered. God doesn't try to pretend that the loss has not taken place. Instead of the wounds being covered over, you are made whole within the context of your new shape.

How are we changed and made whole again? God accomplishes this restoration through spiritual intimacy. This inside-out change is a benefit of the intimacy created through our relationship with God.

Your spiritual life and faith in God are your most powerful allies in your healing journey. God cares about you deeply and wants you to enjoy the best life possible, full of meaningful relationships, joy-filled adventures, and inspiring work that enriches the world.

## Essential Ideas . . . and Your Insights

1. **When we deepen our relationship with God, we find an essential source of healing and power.** This is not a spiritual cliché—it is an vital component of healing from trauma. That is because faith forms in the fires that test what we believe. We form our beliefs in our minds as we learn new things, understand new teachings, and become convinced of new concepts. Faith comes from a deeper place—within our heart and soul. We place our trust in God. We place our lives in his hands.

   **Your response:** What kind of journey have you experienced so far with God? How has your faith journey evolved over time? What emotional response do you have to the idea of choosing to believe in a loving, personal God?

   _____

   _____

   _____

   _____

   _____

   _____

2. **Prayer provides relief for your past hurts and resilience for your future pursuits.** Everybody feels down and distressed now and then, especially when working through the pain of trauma. But sometimes ordinary gloom turns serious—and the trouble begins. It's a self-reinforcing state in which hurricane-force winds push us back two steps for every one we take forward. When we are depressed, we don't *feel* like eating right, getting together with friends, watching a funny movie, or taking a brisk walk in the sunshine.

   And we certainly don't feel like *praying*. "What's the use?" we ask despondently. We are convinced that this time God really has abandoned us.

   Of course, declining to pray when you are in emotional distress is like sitting in a restaurant, near starvation, and refusing to talk to the waiter. A counterproductive behavior if ever there was one! The Comforter you need is the very one you shun.

   **Your response:** In the midst of distress and depression, prayer is a source of serenity and strength you can pursue at any time. What part of your life does prayer occupy? Do you regularly turn to God in times of trouble? How do you think prayer can strengthen you as you seek emotional healing?

   _____

   _____

   _____

   _____

   _____

   _____

   _____

3.  **When you pray, take time to listen.** What you hear can change your life. In our hectic and harried society, most people don't stop and take time to listen deeply enough. To each other. To nature. And especially to God. Listening closely to God's voice will most definitely move you along on your healing journey.

    As with any polite conversation with a friend, at least some of our prayer time should be spent listening. What good is it to pour out our hearts to God if we never wait around to hear his wise guidance? Granted, God doesn't speak exactly as we do, so learning to listen takes some practice. It may help you to keep the following in mind.

    **Your response:** How often do you set aside time to listen to God? Since most people do not hear God's voice speaking to them audibly, in what ways can he speak to you and guide you? What are some specific ways you might make listening a larger part of your prayer life?

    _____

    _____

    _____

    _____

## Taking Stock

What kind of faith activities are you currently pursuing? Check the box besides any of the actions you do at least once a week. If you do something at least weekly that is faith-related and it is not on the list, feel free to add it at the bottom:

☐ Talk to God

☐ Listen for His responses

☐ Practice gratitude

☐ Read the Bible or a devotional book

☐ Come clean about your mistakes

☐ Spend time with like-minded people who share your faith

☐ Serve others

☐ Cultivate a joyful heart

☐ _____

☐ _____

If you are not taking three or more actions every week to practice your faith, consider re-evaluating your spiritual pursuits as a way to promote your healing and wholeness.

## Change Your Story, Change Your Life

1. Describe what you have believed about your soul and your spiritual journey so far. If you have beliefs that you suspect are untrue (or hope are untrue) how did you come by these beliefs in the first place?

_____

_____

_____

_____

_____

_____

_____

_____

2.  Now write out a different narrative you want to embrace. Where do
    you want to end up? Describe your ideal future and destination.

_____

_____

_____

_____

_____

_____

_____

## Dig Deeper

1.  What do you think about the idea that you are not alone, that there
    is a loving God who longs for a relationship (or perhaps a deeper
    relationship) with you? If this were indeed true, how might it change
    how you live your life, or how you feel about your life?

_____

_____

_____

2.  Think back in your life. What has made you feel connected with something—or someone—bigger than yourself? Are there things you've done in the past to nurture your soul that, for whatever reason, you've stopped doing?

    These might include walks in nature, going to church, praying, reading books, keeping a gratitude journal, playing an instrument, worshipping, or volunteering or ministering in your community. Perhaps there was a season in your life when your soul felt nurtured because you were in a community that focused on these things.

    Let your mind wander back through the years, and see if there are things that at one time helped your spirit thrive which are no longer a part of your life:

    _____

    _____

    _____

    _____

    _____

3.  Review your list above. How did these healthy, soulful activities affect your life? What changed? What would happen if you began doing one or more of these things again?

    _____

    _____

    _____

    _____

    _____

4. Do you know other people whose faith in God has been a positive experience for them and those around them? Write the names of these people below:

_____

_____

_____

5. If you could tell God anything, what would you tell him? Write it below.

_____

_____

_____

## First Steps, Next Steps

Now it's time to get practical. We've explored many issues that prompted you to ponder and process. Let's put those thoughts into action. We'll provide several steps forward, and then it's your turn to determine three additional actions you will take this week.

1. Talk to God. Tell him about the things that are concerning you. Thank him for good things in your life. Ask him for help in battling feelings of depression. Ask him to increase your faith.

_____

_____

_____

2.  Remember the list of people whose faith in God has been a positive experience for them and those around them? Reach out to one of these people. Tell that person you are exploring ways to increase your faith and see how the conversation develops from there.

_____

_____

_____

_____

_____

3.  This week, make a difference in the lives of others. Find someplace you can serve, or otherwise reach out to people who would be thrilled to experience a helping hand from you.

_____

_____

_____

_____

_____

4.  Your turn. What steps do you intend to take this week to move toward wellness?

    a.  _____

        _____

        _____

b. _____

_____

_____

c. _____

_____

_____

## Closing Reflections

This powerful verse appears in the book of Proverbs: "Hope deferred makes the heart sick" (13:12). And how true this is! When hope is lost and despair descends, the impact can be devastating and even terminal. And yet with hope, people not only discover new resiliency, they can find themselves surviving and even thriving once again.

If you have not considered yourself a person of faith to date, now may be the moment to change that. I know from my own personal experiences that faith and a relationship with God has been the life preserver I've hung onto in some of the roughest seas of life.

We can place our hope in a lot of things—our own smartness, guidance from others, degrees, money, man-made plans, even people we love. And yet when these things fail—and at some point they will—it's good to have chosen to believe in a God who really does, like the old song says, have the whole world in His hands.

## Scripture for Meditation

"Why, my soul, are you downcast? Why so disturbed within me? Put your hope in God, for I will yet praise him, my Savior and my God."

PSALM 42:11

## Wise Words to Awaken Your Spirit

"You never know how much you really believe anything until its truth or falsehood become a matter of life and death to you."

C. S. LEWIS

## Journal Your Journey

This week you are going to be trying out new things, taking steps forward, forging new habits, and letting go of old ones. Will these things make a difference? Will you be able to discern any changes in how you feel and what you think?

This page is here for you to journal about the journey. What works? What doesn't? You'll know what to keep doing because you'll have your adventure documented in the pages of this workbook. Use this space to ask questions, make lists, doodle, write about your progress, and record milestones.

Let the adventure begin!

_____

_____

_____

_____

_____

_____

_____

_____

_____

_____

_____

_____

_____

_____

_____

_____

_____

_____

_____

_____

_____

_____

_____

# Revive Your Dreams

*As You Look Ahead, Make Hope a Daily Choice*

**Review chapter 9 and "A Closing Word" in the *Triumph over Trauma* book**

## Week 12 at a Glance

Nearly all trauma survivors are at high risk of floundering in life by getting stuck in their past. This becomes a "secondary trauma," as the initial pain leads to adverse aftereffects that ripple through life.

When a person is subjected to trauma, it can lead to a gloomier view of the future. The perception of one's life becomes filled with negative thoughts, such as "I'll never find the love of my life" or "I'll never have a great career" or "I'm always going to be stuck in this dumpy little town." This perception dampens a person's projection of what their life could be and should be. And in that sense, it's a skewed view of both present circumstances and things to come.

If this all sounds discouraging, there is great news for you: Hope for a fulfilling, joyful, productive future is always available.

Hope is a *decision* based on the certainty of an unseen future. The dictionary defines hope as "expectation of fulfillment or success." That word *expectation* clearly indicates the outcome is in the future. Because the outcome lies in the future, it is not visible in the present.

Hope is expecting with confidence something you can't yet see. A Scripture tells us, "Now faith is confidence in what we hope for and assurance about what we do not see" (Hebrews 11:1). Hope, then, is not a reaction based upon an experienced present but a response based upon an expected future.

If your dreams for the future have been dimmed because of trauma, you can revive your dreams with a robust blend of hope, faith, and resilience.

## Essential Ideas . . . and Your Insights

1. **Without hope for tomorrow, we are hindered in our day-to-day ability to undertake the small steps that lead to a positive future.** We develop a "what's the point?" attitude once hope is dampened. This negative experience can have far-reaching consequences in the life of a trauma survivor. A dimmer outlook on life and the future can leave us stuck in disappointment for years and even decades. Finding the motivation to sustain long-term activities—such as finishing school or saving for the future—becomes extremely difficult.

   **Your response:** Do you feel that your trauma experiences have adversely affected your view of the future? Do you find yourself doubting your options and possibilities in life, even if that doesn't align with your talents and intelligence? Do you have irrational negative thoughts that don't match up with reality?

   _____

   _____

   _____

   _____

   _____

2. **For those who have endured trauma of any kind, hope for a future of fulfillment and freedom is essential.** Tomorrow will be better than today, and next year will be much better than this year. Healing takes time, and healing takes hope.

      **Your response:** What is your current perspective of your future? Do you agree that "tomorrow will be better than today"? What will help you develop more hopefulness and optimism as you look forward?

   _____

   _____

   _____

   _____

   _____

3. **Hope is a learned response gained through suffering, perseverance, and trust in a loving God.** In some ways, hope has its most potent power in response to our pain and problems.

      **Your response:** Have your traumatic experiences caused you to stay stuck—or caused you to grow? Or in some ways, both? In what ways has your pain caused you to become stronger?

   _____

   _____

   _____

   _____

   _____

## Taking Stock

A brighter future awaits anyone who stops letting past difficulties and disappointments determine their future. The following questions will help you see the obstacles in your way—and see that you have the power to clear them and move on.

Things I loved to do when younger:
1.

2.

3.

4.

My reasons for stopping those things:
1.

2.

3.

4.

Things that would make me happy now if money/time/the approval of others were no obstacle:
1.

2.

3.

4.

Possible reasons why I am alive on earth (hint: gifts and talents you possess that the world needs):
1.

2.

3.

4.

Excuses I've made for not pursuing my dreams and purpose:
1.

2.

3.

4.

What I fear it would cost to boldly followed my dreams:
1.

2.

3.

4.

What I secretly hope I might gain:
1.

2.

3.

4.

Steps I can take today in the direction of my dreams:
1.

2.

3.

4.

Things I can do in the next year (five, ten, twenty years) to stop sitting on the sidelines of my life and get in the game:

1.

2.

3.

4.

My answers to anyone (including myself) who says I can't achieve all this and more:

1.

2.

3.

4.

## Change Your Story, Change Your Life

1.  What is the story you tell yourself about your dreams for the future and purpose in life? Has your story evolved through the years? What experiences have influenced your thinking about your direction in life? How has trauma changed your perspective about your future? Write out your story—just let it flow without self-editing or filtering.

   _____

   _____

   _____

   _____

   _____

_____

_____

_____

_____

_____

_____

_____

## Dig Deeper

1. How do you think your trauma experiences have affected your outlook on your future? As you experience progress toward wellness, do you feel more enthusiasm about your life as you look ahead?

_____

_____

_____

_____

_____

_____

_____

_____

_____

2.  Many people believe that joy comes naturally and effortlessly into
    our lives. But often we must *choose* joy and intentionally find ways
    to experience it. So this week, how can you invite joy into your life?
    Write out several specific ideas.

    _____

    _____

    _____

    _____

    _____

3.  I ended chapter 9 with an exercise: "Project yourself into the future
    by creating a vision board. The concept of foreshortened future
    means lacking optimism and hopefulness, maintaining a negative
    perspective about what will happen in the years to come. One way
    to regain hope is by creating a vision board—a poster or computer
    printout that includes pictures, quotations, and Scripture verses that
    depict what you want for your bright future. Find images and quotes
    in magazines and online, or create them yourself." If you worked on
    your vision board, describe what you included and why. What else
    would you like to include? If you haven't started on your board, write
    down some ideas about what you would put on it. What images and
    words will help you create a hopeful, exciting vision of your future?

    _____

    _____

    _____

    _____

    _____

4.  It's likely trauma has stolen your desires from you—and it's time to take them back. Reclaiming your desires is really about remembering what you *love*. When you were a kid, nobody could stop you from doing what you loved, which might have been drawing, roller-skating, playing board games, or doing crafts. Write some of your favorite activities from childhood, and think about doing some of them again, all these years later. Recapturing a childlike spirit will make you a happier adult.

    _____

    _____

    _____

    _____

    _____

5.  I pointed out that every trauma survivor struggles and that these struggles eventually make us stronger, if we'll allow them to. That means you need not live forever with pain and regret, but rather with hope that you've survived the ordeal in order to be stronger and better than ever. Record some of the ways the challenge of trauma recovery has taught you important lessons and made you a stronger person.

    _____

    _____

    _____

    _____

    _____

# First Steps, Next Steps

Now it's time to get practical. We've explored many issues that prompted you to ponder and process. Let's put those thoughts into action. I'll provide several steps forward, and then it's your turn to determine three additional actions you will take this week.

1. It's remarkable how often people have trouble finishing the simple sentence, "I want. . . ." Somehow, the process of growing up teaches most of us to think of what we want out of life as secondary to . . . well, just about everything and everyone else. But desire is the fuel that powers achievement. To test yourself for lost connection to your desires, write in the space below several sentences that begin with "I want. . . ." The only rule is you can't write something that's for someone else. Each item must reflect something you want for yourself.

_____

_____

_____

_____

_____

2. Here's the secret to reviving your dreams: Start by looking again at the list you made of things you have loved in your life. Chances are, what you're meant to do now is something you couldn't stop doing as a younger person, but which you abandoned along the way. Or, it may be the thing you still didn't dare put on the list, but which tugs at your sleeve anyway. Write down some things you felt passionate about in the past that might be revived now.

_____

_____

_____

_____

_____

3. Find a friend who will join you in pursuing a new activity—an art class, a new hobby, or something else that is both fun and challenging. Name some people who you can ask to join you, and list possible activities.

_____

_____

_____

_____

_____

4. Your turn. What steps do you intend to take this week to move toward wellness?

   a. _____

   _____

   _____

   b. _____

   _____

   _____

c.   _____

     _____

     _____

## Closing Reflections

I've worked with hundreds of people who were unfulfilled with their lives. They felt dissatisfied and disappointed. Though these men and women generally worked hard doing good things, they had a nagging sense that they were missing out on something.

Indeed, many people struggle with the questions, "What am I really here for? What's my unique purpose and calling?" They want to do something meaningful and significant with their lives . . . but what? And of course trauma has a way of clouding our vision and diminishing our self-esteem, putting a sense of purpose further out of reach.

That's why prayer, reflection, and journaling can be so helpful. Creating the space in your life to explore, contemplate, and dream enables you to determine and define what exactly will be your remarkable contribution to the world. When you tune out all the voices around you screaming for attention, you can listen to your own inner voice and the voice of God. When you are vitally aware of what's going on within you and in your surroundings, your reason for living will become distinctly evident.

When you discover your unique God-given purpose, the excitement of life returns and depression recedes. You know that each day presents opportunities to fulfill your potential and move you in positive direction. That is the joyful life God intends for you—one full of hope for the future.

# Scripture for Meditation

"Rejoice in hope, be patient in tribulation, be constant in prayer."

ROMANS 12:12

# Wise Words to Awaken Your Spirit

"Your hopes, dreams, and aspirations are legitimate. They are trying to take you airborne, above the clouds, above the storms, if you only let them."

WILLIAM JAMES

# Journal Your Journey

This week you are going to be trying out new things, taking steps forward, forging new habits, and letting go of old ones. Will these things make a difference? Will you be able to discern any changes in how you feel and what you think?

This page is here for you to journal about the journey. What works? What doesn't? You'll know what to keep doing because you'll have your adventure documented in the pages of this workbook. Use this space to ask questions, make lists, doodle, write about your progress, and record milestones.

Let the adventure begin!

_____

_____

_____

_____

# Endnotes

1   Sidran Institute, "Traumatic Stress Disorder Fact Sheet," https://
    www.sidran.org/wp-content/uploads/2018/11/Post-Traumatic-Stress-
    Disorder-Fact-Sheet-.pdf.

2   Mayo Clinic, "Forgiveness: Letting Go of Grudges and Bitterness,"
    November 13, 2020, https://www.mayoclinic.org/healthy-lifestyle/
    adult-health/in-depth/forgiveness/art-20047692.

3   Frederick Buechner, *Beyond Words: Daily Readings in the ABCs of
    Faith* (New York: HarperCollins, 2004), 18.

4   Robert Frost, "A Servant to Servants," *North of Boston* (1914),
    https://www.poetryverse.com/robert-frost-poems/a-servant-to-
    servants.

5   "Post-Traumatic Growth," Psychology Today, accessed March 8,
    2022, https://www.psychologytoday.com/us/basics/post-traumatic-
    growth.

6   Richard G. Tedeschi, Jane Shakespeare-Finch, Kanako Taku, and
    Lawrence G. Calhoun, *Posttraumatic Growth: Theory, Research, and
    Applications* (New York: Routledge, 2018).

# About the Authors

**Gregory L. Jantz, PhD,** is a popular speaker and award-winning author of many books, including *Healing Depression for Life, The Anxiety Reset, So Much to Live For, Healing the Scars of Emotional Abuse*, and *Healing the Scars of Childhood Abuse*. He is the founder of The Center • A Place of HOPE, which was voted among the top ten clinics in the nation for healing depression. For more information about Dr. Jantz and The Center, contact:

www.drgregoryjantz.com
www.aplaceofhope.com


**Keith Wall**, a thirty-year publishing veteran, is an award-winning author, magazine editor, radio scriptwriter, and online columnist. He currently writes full-time in collaboration with numerous best-selling authors. Keith lives in a mountaintop cabin near Manitou Springs, Colorado.

# THE CENTER A PLACE OF HOPE

## Voted Top 10 Facility
For Depression Treatment in the U.S.

With over 37 years of leadership in mental health treatment, The Center • A Place of HOPE is a **Top Ten Facility for Depression Treatment**. Our world-class staff provides professional excellence for the treatment of depression, anxiety, eating disorders, PTSD, trauma, addiction, and more.

### We specialize in treating:

- Depression
- Anxiety
- Eating Disorders
- Trauma & PTSD
- Addiction
- OCD
- Sexual & Emotional Abuse
- Anger Management
- Spiritual Renewal

## Hope & Possibility
Podcast

Dr. Gregory Jantz is the pioneer of **Whole Person Care** and best-selling author of over 45 books.

In his new Hope & Possibility podcast, he shares tools and techniques to help with **Depression, Anxiety, PTSD, Eating Disorders**, and more.

Dr. Gregory Jantz
*Best-Selling Author and Founder of The Center • A Place of HOPE*

**Scan QR code** to listen and subscribe!

1.888.771.5166 | admissions@aplaceofhope.com | www.aplaceofhope.com